About the Author

Born in Edinburgh, Sylvia Robinson spent the first part of her working life as a teacher and lecturer in drama first in Ayr and then in Aberdeen. During the second part she ran a children's theatre as well as a presentation skills training company largely for the oil and gas sector while also working as a freelance presenter and interviewer for Grampian Television and BBC Radio Scotland. She has now retired and returned to live in Edinburgh.

A
SCOTS
SAGA

SYLVIA ROBINSON

First published in 2022 by Ridgedales Publishing

Publishing services provided by Lumphanan Press
www.lumphananpress.co.uk

To Michael

"The dead were and are not. Their place knows them no more
and is ours today.... The poverty of history lies in the quasi-
miraculous fact that once on this earth, once on this familiar spot
of ground, walked other men and women, as actual as we are
today, thinking their own thoughts, swayed by their own passions,
but now all gone, one generation vanishing after another, gone
as utterly as we ourselves shall shortly be gone, like ghosts at
cockcrow."

(from "Autobiography of a Historian"
by G. M. Trevelyan, 1876-1962)

Dickson Family Tree

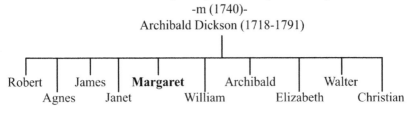

Christian (Chris) Thomson (1718-1799)
-m (1740)-
Archibald Dickson (1718-1791)

Robert	James	**Margaret**	Archibald	Walter
Agnes	Janet	William	Elizabeth	Christian

Turnbull Family Tree

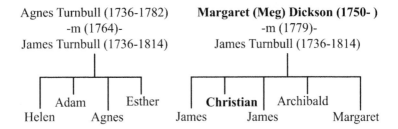

Agnes Turnbull (1736-1782)	**Margaret (Meg) Dickson (1750-)**
-m (1764)-	-m (1779)-
James Turnbull (1736-1814)	James Turnbull (1736-1814)

Adam	Esther	**Christian**	Archibald
Helen	Agnes	James	James	Margaret

Anderson Family Tree

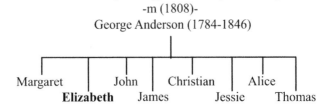

Christian (Christy) Turnbull (1784-1844)
-m (1808)-
George Anderson (1784-1846)

Margaret	John	Christian	Alice
Elizabeth	James	Jessie	Thomas

Dodd's Family Tree

Elizabeth (Betsy) Anderson (1811-1891)
-m (1849)-
Rev. Andrew Dodds (1846-1876)

Christian

Waugh Family Tree

Christian (Chrissie) Dodds (1848-1924)
-m (1872)-
Allan Waugh (1842-1920)

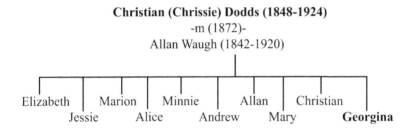

Elizabeth | Marion | Minnie | Allan | Christian
Jessie | Alice | Andrew | Mary | **Georgina**

Flannery Family Tree

Georgina (Ina) Waugh (1890-1966)
-m (1916)-
John Flannery (1894-1980)

Christian (Kitty) Flannery (1917-2012)
-m (1939)-
David Somerville (1917-1941)

-m (1942)-
Ferguson Mackie (1913-1968)

-m (1968)-
Dr Richard Walker (1914-1972)

Christian Thomson

Margaret Dickson

Christian Turnbull

Elizabeth Anderson

Christian Dodds

Georgina Waugh

Christian Flannery

Scottish Naming Patterns in the 18th and 19th centuries

Males

First-born son takes his father's father's name

Second	mother's father's name
Third	father's name
Fourth	father's eldest brother's name
Fifth	father's second oldest brother's name

Females

First-born daughter takes her mother's mother's name

Second	father's mother's name
Third	mother's name
Fourth	mother's eldest sister's name
Fifth	mothers second eldest sister's name

Sometimes when a child died, the next child of that gender born into the family was given the same name as the deceased child. Occasionally two or more living children in the family were given the same name. When they were christened, children were usually given one or two given names.

Contents

Part 4: Elizabeth's Story

Part 5: Chrissie's Story

Part 6: Georgina's Story

Part 7: Kitty's Story

Prologue

January 1796

"Mistress, have you heard what's happening? They're saying the river has overflowed its banks and is sweeping parts of the old Hassendeanburn Kirkyard away! Oh, Mistress, what shall we do?"

"Morag, quieten down. I'm sure it's not as bad as all that. This is not the first time there have been floods down around the old kirk and I'm sure it won't be the last. Now calm down and help me out of bed."

"But Mistress, they're saying the kists buried there are being washed away down the river. They're saying the waters have forced the lids open and bones are appearing. They're saying some widower from Denholm on his way to getting married again at Minto Kirk spied his first wife's kist in the flood when he was crossing the bridge over the river!"

Chris sat up and swung her legs to the floor. If this was true, then this was something different. Certainly the rain had been exceptionally heavy. The wind had been extremely high the previous day and night, but surely Morag's stories were invented. Certainly there had been warnings over the years of the dangers of burying one's loved ones there, but people had ignored them and continued to use the old churchyard. Only five years ago, Archie had been interred there too. Where was his coffin now?

Chris reached for her gown and shawl and soon, with Morag's help, she was dressed. Just as she took hold of her walking stick to make her way across to the bedroom door, the clatter of hooves was heard from in front of the house followed by a banging at the front door.

"Away down and open the door, Morag. See who's here at such an hour."

Morag turned towards the door, while Chris's two sons, Robert and James, burst into the room.

"Mother, we don't want to frighten you but the coffins in the graveyard are being churned up by the water. The men are down there now working to save as many as they can. I'm sure Father's coffin will be caught along with others belonging to the family." James shook his head while Robert tried to comfort his mother.

"Well, we have been warned! I knew we should never have buried Father there. It was bound to happen one day. We'll have to go back and lend a hand. We'll get everything sorted out and let you know how we're progressing."

With that, Robert and James disappeared just as fast as they had appeared, leaving Chris shaking and in a state of shock at the news.

Archie's funeral had taken place in Minto Church only five years before after which, as requested, he had been buried alongside his father and mother in the old Hassendeanburn Kirkyard. If their remains were saved, where would they now be buried? Wherever it was, Chris knew she would eventually join them there.

Then she shook her head and a wry smile came across her face. The coffin with Archie's skeleton was perhaps sailing down the Teviot, but did it really matter? It was his soul that counted and she believed firmly that one day soon, wherever their bodies were put to rest, Archie and she would be reunited for eternity. She began to ponder on what Archie's reaction would have been to this calamitous affair. Would he have seen the amusing side? She smiled as she suspected he might.

All the time she nervously fingered the small silver Luckenbooth brooch attached to her gown. It had been given to her by Archie when he had asked her to be his wife. All these years ago she had vowed to wear it for the rest of her life. This she had faithfully done.

With the help of her stick, she carefully made her way to her comfortable chair by the window, lay back and closed her eyes. The strident voices and banging of doors down below began to fade and the warmth and comfort of the room began to blur.

Slowly another scene began to emerge. She found herself in a familiar cold, dark and low ceilinged bedroom, its four foot deep walls blackened by the smoke belching out from the fire burning in the fireplace. She could smell the peat. She could also smell the aroma of baking bread.

Then she realised she was once more back at Chapple Farm: it was her wedding day.

Part 1

Chris's Story

Chapter 1

1740: A Wedding

In summer, the 'sweet and silver' River Teviot would gently wind its way through the Scottish Border country, flickering and glittering in the warm sunshine while smoothly gliding over pebbles and sand. Sometimes it would hop over rocks, sometimes twirl and twist around floating fallen branches as it passed, its glass surface many times broken by the jumping of a salmon or trout. Roxburgh was deemed to be one of the most picturesque counties in the Scottish Borders with its rolling hills and fertile valleys criss-crossed by winding rivers.

But it was winter. It was the 25th December and although Christmas Day was not recognised in Scotland, the people there were getting ready for another celebration.

In Chapple Farm near Lilliesleaf a cock crowed.

Still cocooned in her warm bed with her ice cold nose peeping out, Chris Thomson looked towards the many small panes of the frost framed window and saw a world covered with a thick blanket of snow. A curtain of misty dawn rose over the land; its pristine white snow-clad hills in the distance dotted with many a murky sheep, animals not to be underestimated for they provided the livelihood of most families roundabout.

It was her wedding day and she was about to marry handsome young Archie Dickson of Hassendeanburn House, the young man she had loved from the first day of meeting him as a child.

Archie had spent most of his young life in an attractive two-storied mansion built in the little hamlet of Hassendeanburn. It stood on the side of a hill, sheltered from the cold winter blasts, and facing south to catch the sunshine as the River Teviot flowed by. His father, Robert, once a young tenant farmer from Cavers, had begun a nursery business at Hassendeanburn in 1727, and had purchased the manse and glebe which had formerly belonged to the Hassendeanburn Kirk. To begin with, he had sold the usual vegetables and soon the business began to flourish. Now his sons, Archie and James, were running the business as Robert was ailing and unable to do so. Archie ran the nursery and James ran the branch shop in Hawick in which the nursery produce was sold. It was in the flat above the shop that Archie and she were to begin their married life. For Chris, living in a town would be a new experience, but she was excited about doing so as she knew Hawick to be a thriving and busy town with plenty going on there.

Next door, she could hear some movement. Her brother, William, was already stirring. She knew that normally once dressed, he would go to the kitchen and pour a mug of ale or brandy before venturing outside to check the cattle in the byre and the sheep in the fields. Then at eight, he would come in for his breakfast of gruel or sometimes mutton and bannocks washed down with more ale before beginning his work, sometimes returning as late as seven in the evening for another meal. The fare in summer would be fresh meat and in the winter fowl with leeks, cabbage or kale, always accompanied by barley bannocks or oatmeal cakes with butter and cheese.

However, that day he would not be following his usual routine but hopefully getting ready to accompany her to her wedding.

Although only 19, William was already the tenant farmer of this small farm and his daily routine echoed that of his father's who had farmed at Midshiels, where both he and Chris had been born. The parish stood near the Border dividing Scotland from England and boasted a tower with its many loop-holes from which guns, arrows and missiles were ready to be fired to defend the parish if necessary. The 1707 Union between Scotland and England had brought peace to the area, apart from the time of the Jacobite Rebellion led by the 'Old Pretender', James Stuart. But that had been duly quashed and happened long before.

Both her parents now having passed away, Chris had come to live with William at his farm nearby and it was from here she was to be married.

While she barely remembered her mother, Agnes, she could clearly picture her father. She and William had always been in awe of him and had avoided him at all costs. Like others round about, James Thomson believed that establishing authority through fear would gain his children's obedience, for in the teachings of the Church did it not state God was punishing the children on earth for their own good? Chris had even heard one of her father's cronies say, "Ma bairns, from the youngest to the eldest, love me and fear me as sinners dread death. My look is law."

Chris could still recollect her father, hat on head, sitting in his seat in the chimney corner, while she and William would be whispering fearfully to each other, or standing respectfully before him when answering his questions. Her poor mother had also been in awe of the man. However, in spite of all this, Chris knew her father had always felt strong affection for them all, though it was deeply concealed.

But now she must move. She jumped out of bed, wrapped a shawl about her shoulders and made her way to the window. She glanced down at the open courtyard framed by the house, the granary and byre on one side, and the barn, where the wedding was to take place, on the other. Round the sides of the build-ings nettles and docken leaves were peeping through the snow, and she could hear the fowl pecking in the midden. If she had married in the summer, hollyhocks, columbines and primroses would have encircled the courtyard where the celebrations with friends and neighbours would have taken place. However, this was December and the festivities were to be held in the barn.

Chris smiled. Wasn't December a good month in which to marry? Did the old nursery rhyme not say as much?

'When December snows fall fast, marry and true love will last.'

While both the farms in which Chris had lived were not much more than crofts, she was aware that she was marrying into a family with considerably more wealth than she was used to. She clearly remembered her first visit to the Dickson home and how she had marvelled at its splendour. It had a drawing room with carpets on the floor, fine mahogany furniture brought from England, and everywhere light streamed in from large windows framed with heavily embroidered curtains. On the walls, and next to several rich tapestries, hung a number of paintings in substantial wooden frames.

She also remembered how Archie's mother, a keen cook, had taken her outside to her herb garden with its rosemary, sweet-basil, fennel, sage, mint and marjoram grown alongside camomile, horse-hound, catmint, eucalyptus, thistle, rue and celandine.

Like her future mother-in-law, Chris could also cook, but her meals were simple fare and she knew she would have to learn how to prepare more advanced meals if she were to feed Archie properly and to entertain in the manner of Hassendean-burn. However, she knew Archie and his family would welcome and support her.

On that first visit to Hassendeanburn House she had been served tea poured from a silver tea pot into cups of porcelain, so unlike the pewter implements of Chapple Farm. She now knew that some medical men believed the beverage was not good for the digestion, while ministers of the Church disapproved of it altogether. She had never drunk the exotic beverage until then, it being an expensive commodity, but that afternoon she had learned it could be bought for less than the usual 25 shillings a pound (still too dear for her purse) from smugglers bringing it into the country from abroad.

In contrast to her own rather cold, stark and loveless home, Hassendeanburn House and the family who lived there were warm and welcoming. Archie's father, now an old man, was unlike her own father and he and everyone else there had genuinely rejoiced in her becoming part of the family.

All week at Chapple Farm, preparations had been carried out in readiness for the wedding. Although the actual event would take place in the best room in the house, the rest would happen in the barn.

Already she could smell the newly baked bread coming from the kitchen. Mary, the cook, with the help of Myra and John, the maid and her husband, was getting ready for the big day and had been planning the feast for many weeks. The guests would be offered milk broth made of barley, followed by another barley broth of beef mutton. Then rounds of beef, legs of mutton and fowl would appear, accompanied by an abundance of oatcakes, the meal concluding with a pudding and lashings of cream. As for drink, throughout the meal the guests would be offered home-brewed ale. Later, whisky and punch in wooden punch bowls would be served to toast the young couple. This no doubt would be followed by round after round of toasts to anything anyone cared to name.

Later, when the barn was cleared of tables, everyone would join in the singing and dancing as was the custom. Sometimes bridegrooms would even sing on their own, a song like 'I Hae a Wife o' My Ain' or 'Some Say that Kissings a Sin', but Chris knew Archie would not be tempted to entertain the assembled guests for he would rather get on with the dancing. He and Chris would be expected to lead off with 'The Bonny Breist Knots', to be followed by everyone dancing petronellas, eight-some reels and, of course, the dreaded 'Strip the Willow', the girls all praying they would not be flung across the room by partners who had imbibed too much.

Although not a holiday as such, friends and neighbours around would treat it as one and join in the celebrations, little caring what was happening in the wider world, for today there was a wedding to celebrate right in their midst. The three principal domestic events – marriage, birth and death – provided rare holidays and opportunities for social gatherings in a life which, for the most part, was an unceasing round of toil. So a wedding was an important occasion and, although invitations were not required, everyone attending was expected to contribute some money. Wedding celebrations in some districts could go on for nearly a week, but Chris knew this would not be happening at her wedding for soon she would be taken away to start her new life with her beloved Archie.

Enough of dreaming: Chris had to get ready if she was to be on time. But where was Jean, her old childhood friend from school, who was to be her bridesmaid? To calm herself, Chris tried to concentrate on all the traditional details required in getting dressed. So much superstition was attributed to this important day and she had no intention of courting ill luck. She took down her stiffly-embroidered floral patterned wedding dress with its Brussels fine lace at both neck and sleeves, and she knew from the old superstitions that her choice of colour was good: 'Married in white, you have chosen right.'

Suddenly she heard a knock at the door and on opening it she found Jean beaming with excitement and energy, her red hair bouncing as she rushed into the room. She carried a gown similar to Chris', for both knew of another superstition that bridesmaids were supposed to dress in a similar fashion to the bride in order to act as a decoy and confuse the evil spirits and fairies, thus protecting the bride.

"I'm here! I'm here! Let's get ready Chris. This is your big day!"

Jean placed her dress on the bed and turned to give Chris a big hug. Then they got dressed together, first in their new linen shifts over which went hoops followed by many petticoats. Then came the corsets and although slightly uncomfortable, they both knew these garments were particularly necessary to produce the desired effect.

"Thank goodness we don't have to wear this normally. Imagine trying to do our work in the farm wearing this," chuckled Jean as she pulled the laces of Jean's corset very tightly.

"Jean, I want to breathe!"

"It's all worth it, my lass. You'll look braw."

"That's as may be, but I don't want to end up fainting at Archie's feet."

Then they donned their new silk stockings before helping each other into their gowns. Carefully, Jean pulled Chris's wedding dress into position before taking some time to fasten the many tiny buttons from neck to waist. On went their new shoes and, just as Chris sat down to have her hair curled into fashionable ringlets, Jean stopped and looked towards the window. The sound of horses' hooves could be heard down in the courtyard followed by voices and laughter.

Jean rushed forwards to see who had arrived.

"It's all the Dickson clan and don't they look grand? There's Archie with James. Oh my, Chris, they both look so handsome."

Chris got up with the intention of moving to the window but quickly Jean barred her way.

"Keep away from the window. You know it's bad luck to see your groom! Now sit down and I'll dress your hair and then put on your pinner, wherever it is."

She did not have to look far for the fine white lace cap was already on the table in front of her. Once placed on Chris's head, Jean carefully lifted the wedding veil from a chair and secured it on top of Chris's pinner and ringlets.

"Something old (your mother's ring), something new (your dress),

Something borrowed…"

Jean frantically looked around the room and then tugged a delicate white handkerchief from her own wrist and gave it to Chris.

"Here, take my handkerchief.

… Something blue (your stockings)."

Jean chanted the old rhyme before turning to her dear friend and giving her a huge hug.

"Now we're all done and just look at you. The perfect bride! Now only have a quick peek at yourself in the looking-glass. Anything longer will bring ill luck."

"But not before I put on something else."

Chris crossed to the dressing table, opened a little box and took out a small silver betrothal brooch.

"Archie bought this for me from a booth standing close to St Giles Cathedral. It's called a Luckenbooth brooch. Look, both our names are engraved on it."

They both stopped for a minute and admired the silver betrothal token with its two entwined hearts of garnets and crystals.

"I vowed to Archie to wear it forever."

"It's braw, lass. And you're braw too!"

There was a loud knock at the door and Jean rushed to open it. There stood William looking unusually and uncomfortably smart in his wedding attire, very different from his regular old working clothes.

Jean took a step back and giggled.

"Oh, William, forgive me but I've never seen you look quite such a gentleman!"

William smiled awkwardly for he had always had a fondness for Jean. Then he looked behind her to his sister.

"You're as bonnie as the Queen of the May, sister. Now take my arm and let us go down to the parlour where the family are waiting for the wedding to begin."

Before doing so, Chris took a quick glance in the looking glass and what she saw pleased her enormously. Yes, she was ready to be queen for the day, but also to be Mrs Archibald Dickson for the rest of her life.

Chapter 2

1750: A Birth

In April, another child joined the ever-growing Dickson family. Archie and Chris already had two sons and two daughters: Robert, now eight, called after Archie's father; Agnes, seven, after Chris's mother; James, four, after her father; and Janet, just two, after Archie's mother. Already, two names had been chosen for the new addition. If he was a boy he would be called William, after Chris's brother; if a girl, Margaret, after Archibald's sister who had died at a young age.

Chris had little recollection of how she had passed the time during her four previous confinements. When expecting her son James in 1746, little was interrupted even by the news of Bonnie Prince Charlie's arrival from France with his intention of restoring the Stuart monarchy to the British throne. He was, after all, the grandson of James II. Having collected support for his cause, first in the Highlands, particularly from the Catholics and Scottish Episcopalians, he had far less success on reaching the Lowlands, for most people there were Protestants and supporters of the present King George. Although causing the king to flee from London the whole situation had ended in one of the bloodiest battles ever fought on British soil.

At the time Chris had little interest in what was going on, but the men folk had much to say. She did, however, remember reading the report of the Battle of Culloden in 'The Caledonian Mercury'. The Prince had survived the battle and returned to France, with most people in the Borders hoping he would never return.

That had been in 1746. Now only four years later, here she was once more expecting a child but no longer living above the shop in the High Street. She and Archie had moved to Hassendeanburn House to join Mrs Dickson when Archie's father had died. Archie had inherited the house as well as the nursery and was now of course the laird of Hassendeanburn. Meanwhile his brother, James, had become laird of their father's other estate at Huntlaw.

Archie had continued to run the thriving nurseries and James the shop, although James already had plans to set up a similar business in Perth. Walter, their youngest brother, now nearly 20 years of age, was aiming to do so in Edinburgh. And while all this was going on, Archie and James still had time to become agents for the newly formed British Linen Bank in Hawick.

Chris looked down at the bump beneath her gown and patted it contentedly. But then she sighed at the thought of having to endure another visit from Tibbie, the trusty midwife, with all her superstitions and warnings. She, along with Mrs Dickson Chris's mother-in-law and two friends, would again be present to help as at the four previous births. While Chris was eternally grateful for their support, she did nevertheless miss her own mother's presence to offer guidance during these ordeals.

She knew well what to expect from Tibbie's superstitious preparations. As before, the bedchamber would be the birthing room with all the doors and windows closed in order to retain warmth, as well as repelling evil influences. At Robert's birth, Chris recalled, Tibbie had even tried having the curtains closed to blot out the moonlight in order to protect the child, but as it was the middle of the night and the candles were insufficient to be able to see by, the curtains were re-opened. The fire was sure to be lit to provide heat and, even more importantly, to caudle the brew of alcohol, sugar and spices which would be offered to the assembled company helping with the birth.

Chris sat back and pictured Tibbie arriving with her usual assortment of herbs. Some would be to ease the child into the world, others to help her cope with the pain. Sea herbs, mugwort, vervain, penny royal and no doubt an eagle stone, some jasper and some coral would all be found in Tibbie's voluminous bag, along with certain stones which would be attached to particular parts of Chris' body to draw the baby down into the womb.

After the birth, much attention would be paid to cutting the umbilical cord, for it had to be performed in a certain way. If a boy was born, then a longer length was left to encourage a longer penis to grow and to ensure future potency. Chris would be instructed to make sure the palms of her hands did not touch the boy while bathing him, thus causing his prosperity to be washed away. If a girl was born, Tibbie would make sure, as she had done with baby Agnes, to wrap her in one of Archie's old shirts thus ensuring a prosperous marriage.

Although all these rituals were not due to take place for a couple of months, Chris reminded herself to tell Archie to offer everyone something to eat once the drama was all over. He, of course, would not be joining the ladies in the bedchamber for his role, as was the custom, was to provide the 'blether meat' or the private feast for the women. Meanwhile, Annie the cook would have the 'groaning' cheese ready to offer to the visitors who were bound to call several days later and to make sure it would be sliced for the unmarried women to put under their pillows to help them dream of their future husbands.

But would Archie remember all this? She very much doubted it, for he had other things to think about. Anyway, she knew she could rely on his mother to organise these domestic proceedings leaving Archie free to get on with working on his business catalogues, which listed all the articles for sale and the prices. The list of trees and plants had grown considerably since they were first married, for now they were selling ash, apple, cherry, elm and oak trees, as well as the usual peas, beans, cabbages, potatoes, leeks and turnips. Now he had gained two important customers, the Duke of Argyll and the Earl of Marchmont, both having submitted large requests for their immense estates.

To take her mind off the forthcoming event, Chris turned to the newspaper and found an advertisement for George Roe's warehouse in Cant's Close, Edinburgh, offering a list of newly arrived clothes. This was much more interesting than thinking of Tibbie and her superstitions.

"Rich brocades and damasks of the newest patterns," she read, "in black Genoa and Dutch velvets, scarlet cloaks and velvet caps, poplins, embossed serge for petticoats, silk stockings and hand-kerchiefs, and a choice of the ribbons in the newest fashion."

Reading came easily to Chris, as it did to most of the population for Scotland prided itself on providing education for both boys and girls. Unfortunately, however, the skill of writing was not provided, although there were some women of her generation who could write letters and keep diaries, but they were daughters of the gentry and had been brought up as ladies. She, on the other hand, had been the daughter of a tenant farmer and had received no such education. She had been brought up to work on the farm without the luxury of time to sit and entertain herself with books, music and samplers.

Archie of course, being a man, had been taught to both read and write. How much easier it would have been if she had been able to write for she could have helped him with his accounts, allowing him more time to tend to his plants or meet his customers. She vowed at that moment she would make sure her daughters would be able to both read and write.

But then she shook her head. Whatever one's station in life, women would always have to face childbirth and all the dangers it entailed. Not only that, after having done so, they would still be barred, as custom dictated, from the immediate celebrations which followed. Once again she would be barred from celebrating this baby's baptism. After all the pain, danger and effort she would endure she would have to stay upstairs while everyone else rejoiced in the baby's birth. Only then, after a month had passed and she had become 'clean' again, would she be allowed to appear once more in public. Chris sighed. The least she could do as a present to herself would be to choose a wonderful outfit to wear on that occasion and so, with this in mind, she returned to the newspaper to plan what she would buy.

A couple of months later a child was born and, although Archie would have preferred another little boy to help him run the business, a little girl appeared. On the Sabbath of a warm summer June morning a month later, Chris as planned stepped into the local church dressed in a cotton burgundy gown of the latest fashion. With its bell-shaped sleeves, pink satin stomacher and matching petticoats intricately embroidered with scattered leaves, she made her way down the aisle in her curved high heels. Round her shoulders, she wore a fine silk fichu, and on her head sat an equally fine delicate muslin cap. In her arms she carried the baby Margaret.

Chapter 3

1778: An Anniversary

Meg came running into the kitchen waving a book in front of her mother and her older sister, Janet. They were about to plan a special family party to celebrate an important birthday event. Archie and Chris were soon to be 60.

"Look what I have!" Meg exclaimed.

"You know I can't read from so far away, Meg. Read it for us both." Chris screwed up her face in exasperation: her eyesight was failing rapidly.

Janet grabbed the book from her sister and read, "'Cooking and Pastry' by Susanna McIver."

"It's just been published," explained Meg, "and everybody's talking about it. James brought it back for us yesterday when he was in Edinburgh admiring that new North Bridge there."

"Did he go over it? You wouldn't catch me near it after what happened to those people a few years ago."

Chris had never visited the capital, but she had heard tell of the plans to create a new town which had involved draining the Nor' Loch and building a multi-arched North Bridge above it. She was referring to a day ten years before when the side walls of the Bridge had collapsed, killing those who were on the bridge at the time.

"Oh Mother, the part that collapsed has now been rebuilt. It's supposed to be well worth seeing, according to James."

Chris shook her head. She had no intention of visiting such a dangerous place for she remembered Archie telling her the reason why the new town was so necessary. Around 35,000 people had been living for years in less than a mile of space and were crammed into crumbling tenements, many of them up to 14 storeys high. She vowed she would never set foot in Edinburgh – neither old town nor new.

"Anyway, the writer of the book is a lady who has a cookery school for young lassies."

"Well done. Now both of you have a peek and see if you can find something fine we can serve at the party. Something really tasty an' then we'll have to check we've got all the ingredients."

Her daughters eagerly flipped through the pages, their eyes sparkling brightly with anticipation. It was not long before Meg came across a recipe which interested her.

"What about this one? It's called Sir Robert Walpole's Dumplings and it says, 'a rum cocktail mix – a very tasty variation of suet puddings made from breadcrumbs and whipped eggs'."

"That sounds good. And what do we need?"

"Shredded suet, breadcrumbs, dried currants, candied orange peel, candied citron peel, eggs, salt and lard."

"Well, that'll do grand but what else could we have?"

Meg turned a few more pages and then suggested,

"What about cock-a-leekie broth? That needs a cock, leeks, prunes, Jamaica pepper, salt and a bay leaf."

"Aye, anything else? Any other good ideas in your book?" asked her mother.

Meg soon came upon one.

"Here's a recipe for potted heid. This needs an ox head, a foot, salt, pepper, cayenne, mustard, a bay leaf, mace, cloves and water. What about that?"

"Aye, that sounds like just what is needed. Check with Mary down the stair and see she's got all the ingredients before we begin."

Janet began counting on her fingers.

"Is everybody coming this year? How many of the family will be invited? You and Father, Meg, Archie, Walter, Christian and me. Robert won't be home, so he's out. Uncle James an' Uncle Walter. Now that Willie is in Perth with Uncle James I suppose he'll be here too. Then there are the three married couples – Agnes and Walter, James and Jean, Betty and Charles. Their children won't be coming, will they?"

Her mother shook her head.

"Then, with all the younger brood here at home, I make it 16!"

"Off you go and see if Mary has the ingredients."

Her two daughters nodded and with a laugh and a shrug left the kitchen giving Chris a little time to sit down and reflect. Her youngest three children, Archie, Walter and Christian, were indeed still at home with the two who had just left the kitchen. Chris wondered if these two older daughters would be staying at home for the rest of their lives, for Janet was now 30 and Meg 28.

Chris smiled contentedly: how lucky she and Archie had been. All their 10 children had survived and most were still living near them, apart from Robert who was at sea and William in Perth. Above all, they were lucky in that they still truly loved one another and were always the greatest of companions.

As she heard the rain sheeting down, she glanced out of the window at the darkening day and saw the branches of the trees bending wildly in the increasing wind. She was glad to be in her warm and cheerful kitchen that day with the fire burning brightly in the corner. But she knew for many people it was a necessity to be outdoors. Those working in the nurseries had to tend to the shrubs and vegetables, and those on the farms had to plough and see to the animals.

Then she noticed the forlorn figure of their neighbour, James Turnbull, passing the house on his way to Greenhouse, his own farm nearby. Poor man. His wife, Agnes, was not long for this world and he and his four children would soon be left to run the farm and fend for themselves. Certainly they were sensible, dependable children, but it would be hard for them to be without a mother.

Chris well remembered the day James and Agnes had arrived at Greenhouse. They had been so full of love, energy and plans for the future. Archie and James had spent many an hour discussing farming, although James was already well acquainted with the subject, his family having farmed for generations. But farming was changing and methods had altered so much since Chris herself had lived on her father's farm in Midshiels. In those days, the mode of cropping and rotation had been very simple with the practice of common grazing, largely to provide their own food for their own families. Now, it was regarded as a business, set up not only to feed the immediate families but also to provide for all those who had moved to the expanding towns and cities for work.

Hawick too was growing fast. Workshops and mills were being established for the production of woollen goods. It lay by the fast flowing river Teviot, which provided the waterpower to drive machinery and to wash wool. It was also situated on the main road from Edinburgh to Carlisle, a great boon for distributing products. But most important of all, the surrounding hills provided ideal pasture for the thick-fleeced Cheviot sheep which provided the good quality wool.

Agnes' father, Thomas Turnbull, had set up the Hawick Carpet Company, only one example of the town's many business successes. Another was that of the hosiery industry and, when Bailie John Hardie installed four knitting frames, it certainly looked as if the venture would turn out to be a roaring success.

Young James Turnbull, like many a wise farmer at the time, was aware of the need for grain, butter, milk, cheese, eggs and meat to feed those in the towns. He realised that, if he were to help feed their people, the rotation methods of planting barley, grass, oats and turnip had to be applied in his farm, and that would mean the land would have to be divided into fields. Greenhouse had hedges and dikes and ditches and was becoming a thriving farm. The old 'runrig' system of strips of land had disappeared and the profitable Cheviot sheep were now roaming the hills, while the cattle in the fields provided milk and meat. Meanwhile, grain continued to be gathered and stored ready for market, where it would be sold and made into bread.

James had even invested in an English plough and now Greenhouse was a thriving farm. He had also improved his family's living conditions by knocking down the original old cottage and building a decent-sized dwelling house, with outbuildings for storage and byres for the cattle around a sizeable courtyard. Now, he was quite a prosperous man, both liked and respected by the community.

Meanwhile, Agnes had looked forward to furnishing this lovely new dwelling house and had begun choosing fancy mahogany chairs and tables as well as curtains and hangings of various designs and materials, when suddenly all planning ceased after she became ill. Now, she was lying on her death bed.

Chris shook her head and sighed deeply. Fate was cruel.

"What's wrong, Mother?"

Chris had not noticed Meg coming back into the kitchen.

"Is the thought of all these visitors too much for you?"

"Ah, lassie, I was only minding on the poor Turnbulls. It must be mighty sore for them. I know how kind you have been in giving them help when you can, but they will aye be at a loss without Agnes. They don't deserve such ill luck."

"Aye, it's true, Meg. You've fairly been doing a grand job there."

Chris and Meg turned to see Betty, one of Meg's younger sisters, standing in the doorway. She was staying with them during her confinement.

"And I ken they all love you, but perhaps you'll be hoping to step into their mother's shoes when she dies. You've aye had a fancy for that good man!"

"Lassie, I despair of you sometimes. Stop your blethering.

Stop your havers and show some respect for the dying."

Betty, who had married the 48-year old Charles Scott two years before at the tender age of 19, was now expecting her first baby. She was so unlike her two older sisters in her confident and coquettish manner, for they were growing plainer as they grew older. She had certainly always been the most attractive, with her heart-shaped face and gleaming hair piled up high on her head. But all three daughters, while very different, were all very loving in their own way.

Perhaps Betty was right about Meg. Although Chris was certain Meg would never have wished this tragedy to happen to Agnes Turnbull, perhaps she was indeed hoping that in time her chance would come along and that one day she would take Agnes' place.

But now was not the time for such thoughts. There was much work to be done if these birthday celebrations were to come about. Life had to go on, and so Chris bent down and put more wood on the fire, while leaving her three daughters to continue making more suggestions for the forthcoming feast.

Early one morning, less than a year later, Chris heard a banging at the front door and on opening it found Nelly, the oldest of the three Turnbull children. She stood in the cold bleakness of a January day with one hand tightly clutching a shawl wrapped around her shivering body and the other trying to brush away tears from her cheeks. In between short intakes of breath she managed to stutter that her mother had just died.

After offering as much comfort as she could to the distraught young girl, Chris made her way to Greenhouse followed by her daughters and servants. On their immediate arrival, after greeting James and his children, windows were opened to ease the departure of Agnes' soul but were soon shut again to keep out the cold wind and lashing rain outside. The Dickson women braced themselves for the difficult but necessary task ahead to prepare the body for burial. They would first carefully wash it, then dress it in winding sheets, and finally gently lay it out or "kisten" it, for relations and friends to pay their last respects.

Meanwhile Archie rode to the kirk and arranged for bells to be rung to alert the folk of Agnes' death. He then rode to Hawick to seek out the beadle, to make sure he would go into the town square and ring the dead bell to announce her passing.

Back at Greenhouse, Chris was instructing everyone to draw all the curtains and blinds, which would stay that way until the funeral was over. Then she organised several young women, including Meg, Janet and Christian, her youngest, to take it in turns to sit and watch over the body, in order to keep the spirit from falling to the devil. This 'lykewake' would last several days.

The funeral feast had then to be prepared for, in spite of its being a sad affair, it was also a time of much eating and drinking. Chris knew that whisky and ale must be served to the guests along with bannocks, butter and cheese. Soon, many neighbours would be arriving at the house and the ceremony would begin. Everyone who so wished would have the opportunity to toast Agnes Turnbull, and so a goodly supply of drink and food must certainly be on hand.

Readings from the Bible would have to be chosen and hymns to be sung. Chris delegated Janet to choose the hymns but, as far as the passages were concerned, these must be chosen by James, who at that moment was in no fit state to do so. The dejected widower was sitting by the fireside, bemused and unable to move. His children sat by his side, all like statues and all stunned by the death of their mother. Although they knew it was bound to happen, when the death actually did take place the blow had still been keen.

However, the Turnbull family did manage to cope with the many visitors who arrived at Greenhouse over the next few days to file past the coffin, some even touching Agnes' brow or breast, lest they themselves be haunted by the corpse's spirit afterwards.

Somehow James and his one son, thirteen-year-old Adam, with Archie's help, did manage to choose some passages from the Bible and did manage to read them to the mourners before watching the coffin being finally closed and the black velvet mort-cloth, owned by the parish, placed over it. Eight female relatives then came forward and took the first 'lift' – the old ritual of raising the coffin onto carefully upturned chairs, for fear of Agnes' ghost sitting on them.

Then it was time for the eight male coffin bearers to come forward and gently carry it out of the door feet first as was the custom, so that Agnes' soul could not find its way back home. The funeral procession took place on foot, the bell ringer leading the way, towards Lilliesleaf Kirkyard. Archie Dickson and his sons were among the eight along with Adam, Agnes' only son, but as was the custom of the day, James, her grieving husband, did not attend the funeral but stayed at home by himself privately to mourn the loss of his beloved wife.

Throughout the long winter days and nights that followed, the Turnbulls of Greenhouse went about their everyday lives tending to the farm and as always attended the Lilliesleaf Kirk services on the Sabbath, always supported by neighbours and friends, including Chris and her daughters. Adam continued working hard by his father's side while Nelly, his eldest sister, attempted to run the house and look after her two younger sisters. Life continued almost as it had done before Agnes' death, but now there was no loving mother to care for them.

However, in the following spring, the birds returned from abroad to sing over fields and river once again, the branches on the trees sprouted new leaves and with the reappearance of the warm sun in a peaceful sky, an announcement was made in Lilliesleaf Kirk one Sabbath morning which brought a wave of joy to the small community. James Turnbull of Greenhouse was to marry again. His bride was to be none other than Margaret Dickson of Hassendeanburn. It was true, as Betty had predicted:

"She'd aye had a fancy for that good man!"

And so one morning, at a quiet ceremony in Lilliesleaf Kirk,

Meg Dickson became Mrs James Turnbull. The Church was new, having only been completed in 1771, and with its newness came new hope for the Turnbull family. Meg married the man she had always admired and became step-mother to Adam, Nelly, Nancy and Esther who rejoiced in having Meg in their home, for they had known her forever and loved her all their lives. But they never forgot their mother who lay in Lilliesleaf Kirkyard.

Later that year the Turnbulls were blessed with a little baby called James, after his grandfather and father. Gradually, the farm-house at Greenhouse changed from a place of mourning to one of happiness and love once again.

Chapter 4

1784: A Christening

"But this is a new age of prosperity and progress, Father. The country's economy is booming. Just look at Glasgow's successful tobacco industry. Look at the linen manufacturing here in our own town. Hawick's now a centre of excellence for spinning and weaving, now employing around 20,000 hand-loom weavers."

"Robert's right, Father. Look at the roads, canals and bridges being built. You must admit transportation is so much easier now than it was when you were young."

"Aye, lads, if you believe everything you hear. These news-papers seem to take a great deal of delight in pointing out the weaknesses of the old order, but what about the folk who have tended the land for centuries? What's happening to them? They have to leave their wee bit homes and go to the cities and beyond to find work. Do you call that an improvement?"

"But they don't have to do that, there's work right here in the mills."

"Aye perhaps hereabouts, but what about the poor souls in the Highlands who have been flung out of their homes and have had to sail away from Scotland altogether to survive?"

"Oh Father, don't be such a sentimentalist. They don't have to go abroad. They can go and live round the coast and work in the kelp industry."

"It's true Father, Archie's right. Those emigrating are just panicking and after all they don't own their land."

"And those who do can become prosperous and introduce the Cheviots to their land just as we did."

"But that's just what the landowners are doing, lad. The poor folk have had to leave to make way for the sheep."

Chris hardly listened to this discussion between her husband and two sons for she had heard it so many times before. She turned away and looked round the assembled company, happily chatting and laughing.

Their eldest son, Robert, now living at Huntlaw, was there with his wife, Beatrix Pott, who had managed to extricate herself from the discussion. She had found her sister-in-law, Marion, married to Archie, Chris's fourth son, from whom he had inherited the estate of Housebyres.

Robert and Archie were now joined by James. He and his wife, Christian Turnbull, were now living at Alton but Christian had no interest in the animated conversation either and had also chosen to join the ladies.

Suspecting this male-dominated conversation would continue in a similar vein, Chris also joined the ladies with her two daughters, Agnes and Janet. Agnes, her first-born daughter, had come over from Whitmuirhall with her husband, William, while Janet, her second-born, had come from Flatfield with her husband, Alex. However, neither husband was to be seen but no doubt would be somewhere else in the room also talking politics.

The six ladies were soon joined by Betty, Chris's fourth daughter, there with her husband, Charles Scott of Wauchope, who too disappeared leaving the seven ladies to their 'women talk'. Finally her youngest daughter Christian, still unmarried and still living with them at Hassendeanburn, arrived to join them.

The conversation began with all the births, marriages and

death columns to be found in the 'Scots Magazine' soon to be followed by talk of some of the unfortunates who had recently been forced by the Kirk Session to sit on the repentance stool in the kirk as punishment for fornication or adultery.

"Fancy having to be harangued like that by the minster," tittered her youngest daughter. "And in front of the whole congregation."

"It could be worse." Betty could always be relied upon for especially tasty pieces of gossip. "In some kirks, they are forced to wear that iron collar attached to the kirk wall."

"Oh, you mean 'the jougs'?" Marion also seemed to be well informed.

"On the other hand, the Kirk Session does a good service in that it protects young girls who find themselves with child," added Beatrix. "They find the erring fathers and make them acknowledge the child and pay for its upkeep, which of course saves the parish from having to do so."

"But," interjected Betty, "have you heard about the parish minister in Jedburgh?"

All the ladies turned and looked at her, all shaking their heads. "He was found guilty of adultery and forced to stand on the repentance stool in his own kirk wearing sackcloth on successive Sabbaths."

"No! Imagine having to be so humiliated." exclaimed Christian. They all nodded in agreement, while barely hiding the smirks on their faces.

Chris smiled to herself. The people in the room were so lucky. They did not have to live in fear of being turned out of their homes, either to face unheard-of journeys to foreign countries or to go and live in city slums to toil long hours in unhealthy conditions. Oh no, they had the good fortune to live in the peace and fresh air of a beautiful countryside. No screeching metal and grinding machines for them; instead, only the sounds of mumbling honey bees, tweeting birds and the bleating of sheep on distant hillsides. No sights or smells of poverty or disease for them; instead, they woke up to the beauty of the trees, the colours of the changing seasons and to the sparkling rivers meandering on their way. They were free to breathe in the comforting smell of newly-mown hay and the scent of the many flowers growing nearby. Surely this was very heaven? She and her family were privileged to be there thanks to their grandfather's insight in setting up the nursery. Now the customers included such gentry as the Dukes of Argyll, the Earls of March and Minto, Lord Drummond and others who sought out Archie's help in developing their plantations around the old castles and new mansions.

Now the children, no longer children but middle-aged, were landowners themselves and respected members of the community, as were Archie's brothers, James and Walter, who had gone on to set up their own nurseries in Perth and Leith. James sadly was now dead, but where was Walter? Ah yes, there he was chatting amicably with Chris's other two sons, Walter and William, also both bachelors. Walter was known now as Dickson of Chatto, while William, as Dickson of Bellwood, was in Perth where he was building up the successful horticultural business started by his uncle James.

Chris knew the century was being labelled the Age of Improvement and that many – those who owned land – were turning into very rich people, including members of her family. Many in that room that day were building imposing country houses with towers, with elaborate ceiling mouldings and expensive gold ornamentation. Furniture of beautifully veneered and inlaid mahogany was now being displayed, based on that of the famous Chippendale, Sheraton and Hepplewhite, along with lavish fabrics, delicate china and framed paintings.

With this desire for the ownership of fine houses came a need also for grand estate policies to demonstrate their social position, and who better to help them achieve those than the Dickson Nurseries?

While the wives and daughters enjoyed the luxuries of life,

their men folk discovered that alongside such wealth came political power and influence. Now, Archie and his sons could count themselves as part of the middle classes along with the merchants and professional men.

Certainly, great riches were there for some to enjoy, but Chris was keenly aware that those in the room that day were only part of a lucky tiny minority of the population. The vast majority did not have such luxury: for many, life was more about daily survival. Of course the Dicksons, and Archie in particular, had spent their lives working hard to develop the business and so deserved such rewards, but then so had many others who worked equally as hard but received little in return. But what could be done? What should be done? Many thought the poor were undeserving, often regarded as lazy layabouts who drank their way through life while producing children. They were regarded as having no idea of responsibility, no reverence for their God, no understanding of moral values. Many had that belief and the Church certainly upheld that view.

With her mind on the effects of the demon drink and suchlike, Chris could not help but note the quantity of whisky being imbibed at that very moment by some people who were the first to criticise the poor. Archie had recently told her of how the demand for Scotch whisky was so desperate in the south of the country that 300,000 gallons had crossed the Border recently without the knowledge of the excisemen – or so went the gossip. It was even rumoured that Hawick did a great trade in the commodity, which arrived from the small fishing village of Bouleman near Alnwick on the Northumbrian coast to be exchanged for gin, silks and tobacco. Roxburghshire was scarcely provided with enough constables of the peace to prevent all this, and so smuggling appeared to be rife across the country. There was even talk of an Edinburgh councillor by the name of Mr Deacon Brodie being involved in such goings-on. Of course, for those caught, like the said gentleman, the penalty for such a crime was death by hanging in Edinburgh's Tolbooth.

Chris watched the ladies and admired how delicately they moved around the room in their fashionable gowns, while making polite conversation as they went. What did 'The Scots Magazine' call it again? 'The Revolution of Manners'. She was reminded of an article she had read in the magazine on the merits of learning to speak in the English tongue rather than the Scots. It had gone on to describe how David Hume, the philosopher, and Adam Smith, the economist, among other 'enlightened' thinkers of the time, had argued for the dropping of the old Scots tongue. They believed all efforts should be made to adopt a more cultivated form of speech. They had even tried to rectify this by setting up the Society of Promoting the Reading and Speaking of the English Tongue and hiring elocutionists to rid the gentile and educated Scots society of their Scots tongue. The great English playwright Thomas Sheridan had visited Scotland to offer courses in English, in which he proposed instructing gentlemen in the knowledge of the English tongue, while teaching them to pronounce it with purity and acquiring the art of public speaking. To Chris's surprise, her daughters welcomed the idea, and whether or not they or their husbands ever attended such courses, it became clear as time went on that they themselves were making attempts to modify their own speech. Chris had argued there was nothing wrong with the good Scots tongue, but they had insisted that to get on in society they had to be able to converse with people in the wider world who would not under-stand the mother tongue.

By this time, the wives having joined the husbands, Beatrix, who had recently been unwell, was now speaking.

"I'll be back to normal soon. A little trip to Edinburgh to spoil myself will do the trick. Marion's coming with me for a few days and we're staying in a grand hotel there."

But Archie interjected.

"The city may have its airs and graces, but it's an evil place. I hear rats are running in and out of the houses in the High Street, no matter how grand the folk there think they are in their sedan chairs and all. Just be mindful of the pickpockets that roam about."

"Oh, Archie, don't spoil their fun before they get there."

Chris interjected and then turned to her third son.

"James, you're looking quite the toff today in your fancy waistcoat."

"That's as maybe but before I forget, Mother, I have something to tell you that will make you laugh."

"Go on, son, tell me."

"Did you know that a couple of young lads stopped me in the High Street the other day and asked if that was my grandfather who had written 'Rule Britannia' because the writer is one James Thomson?"

"What? And what was your reply?"

"I thought about saying it was and then told them the truth, although I believe the writer did come from the Borders. Now Father, we're just away to get another dram. Can I fetch you anything?"

No thanks, son, I've a dram here. Now off you young ones go and mix with the party. It's grand to see you all here."

With that, they all moved on as suggested to greet other groups in the room, some relations, some neighbours, no doubt to discuss the state of affairs at home or in America where the War of Independence had ended the previous year. Perhaps too, the subject of the rebellions in France against the extravagance of the king and his family at the Palace of Versailles would be discussed. Would Britain be involved in another war? Chris hoped not.

She quietly made her way outside for a breath of fresh air and for some peace. She sat down on the bench overlooking the river with its smooth surface gently ruffling in the cool breeze, while above the sun was beginning to set behind the distant trees in which the birds gently cooed.

Yes, it was good to see their five sons and four daughters. But what of their fifth daughter? Chris smiled, for she knew well what had happened to Meg. She was missing because she had just given birth to a little baby, whose life they were celebrating that day. As custom still dictated, despite all the sophistication of the present company, she was barred from being present and would be sitting at home in the farm at Greenhouse. She would be there with first-born, James, for company. Sadly, the little lad had been born both physically and mentally disabled and, while the poor wee thing was battling so bravely with life, the doctors thought he had not long left to live. James and Meg had not had an easy life so far, but surely the Turnbulls' fortunes would now take a turn for the better with the birth of their second child, a little girl.

It was good to see her son-in-law so happy again. He had always been proud of being a Turnbull and took great delight in recounting the legend that, during the Wars of Scottish Independence, William of Rule had saved King Robert the Bruce by wrestling a bull to the ground when it had charged at the king. William had not only been rewarded by the name of William Turnbull but had received the lands of Philliphaugh, now part of Selkirk, while assuming a bull's head as his heraldic symbol with the motto 'I Saved the King'. True or not, the Turnbulls went on to become one of the most turbulent of the Border families and in the 16th century the Turnbulls of Barnhills, the notorious Border reivers, built Fatlips Castle in Roxburghshire at the top of the Minto Crags above the River Teviot. The castle was later acquired by Sir Gilbert Eliot in 1705, whose family eventually became the Earls of Minto, the present one now employing the services of the Dickson Nurseries to develop his gardens.

Chris suddenly became aware of someone behind her and on turning round found Archie had come to join her. He sat down beside her and then, with a gentle smile, took her hand. Together, they sat in silence enjoying the tranquillity of the evening. No words were needed as they shared the same thoughts and feelings. They were lucky. In spite of having been together all these years, their love was still as strong as it had always been and their children and families were living near them in the best and most beautiful county of Scotland – or so Chris firmly believed. How satisfied Archie's father, Robert, would have been to see such a family gathering in such a wonderful setting. It was Archie's dearest wish that the business would continue to develop in the skilled and caring hands of their sons, perhaps even extending to those of the fourth generation. Certainly there were plenty of grandchildren around that day, so surely at least one would take up the challenge. But Chris at that moment shuddered. She felt old.

"I know, lass, it's a new world." Archie squeezed her hand and drew it gently to his lips for a comforting kiss.

Then the sound of laughter came towards them. James, their son-in-law, was approaching holding his precious baby girl and accompanied by his three children, Nelly, Nancy and Esther. All were lovely girls, thought Chris, all with their lives before them. Their education had been much wider than her own, for they could write as well as read and had studied history and geography. Not only could they play the spinet and harpsichord, but also the pianoforte. They also had singing lessons and that very day Nelly had entertained the family with a rendition of 'My Mither Bids Me Bind My Hair', while Nancy had sung 'The Flowers of the Forest'.

The three were obviously very proud of this little half-sister of theirs, particularly Esther who pleaded with her father to hold the smiling bundle. This 14-year-old stepdaughter was truly strikingly good looking, dressed in her white cambric gown with its blue silk ribbon matching her piercing azure eyes. Chris reckoned that every day Esther looked more and more like her dead mother Agnes, while also possessing her sweet nature. Eventually the girl's wish was granted and the little bundle was passed to her. She smiled and gurgled at the new-born babe and then, after a little while, bent forward and passed the child to Archie. He held the child gently in his arms, while staring at her in wonder as he had done with all his own children and grandchildren, before eventually passing the baby to Chris. She too smiled fondly at the little thing. Its large blue eyes in its chubby face surrounded by a fancy beribboned and lace cap seemed to stare back with understanding.

What would this little child's life be like? The world and the face of the Scottish countryside were changing so fast. Perhaps she wouldn't stay in Roxburghshire. Perhaps she would leave the Borders and settle elsewhere. In spite of the roaming highwaymen, travel was so much easier now with the building of the 150 new roads. Perhaps she would leave the countryside altogether and live in one of the many towns which were being built, or even move to a city. Would she marry? If so, who would she choose? Where would they meet? All these questions rushed through her mind and Chris doubted if she would be around to discover the answers. Silently, she blessed this tiny girl who had that very day been christened and named after her. She had become another Christian.

Chapter 5

1798: A Day Book

It was still early morning, but Chris had been awake most of the night. The wind and rain had been battling against the window and had no doubt caused the destruction of a number of trees in the nursery, but she knew those working there were practised in coping with such an eventuality.

Sometimes Chris would send herself back to sleep by trying to remember lines of poems she had learnt when she was younger, and so she began reciting the words of one of her favourite poems 'Elegy Written in a Country Churchyard':
"The curfew tolls the knell of parting day,
The lowing herd wind slowly o'er the lea,
The ploughman homeward plods his weary way,
And leaves the world to darkness and to me."
But after the first stanza she could remember no more. Then she tried one Shakespearean sonnet followed by another, but that did not do the trick either.

After tossing and turning for what seemed like hours, she lit a candle by her bedside, intent on reading. Often her Bible would suffice in sending her back to sleep, but then she noticed a few of Archie's books on the table on the other side of the bed. One was his 'Day Book' bound in white leather, which lay there as it had always done when he was alive. He had always kept it there and had written it up at the end of each day. She kept the books there now as a comfort for, although he had managed to stay to celebrate their fiftieth wedding anniversary six years before, from then on he had begun to fade until death took him.

She had never actually taken the time to read his 'Day Book' before but now, having found her spectacles, she opened it and for the first time read the words.

'Robert Dickson, Gardener in Hassendeanburn 1739.'

Then on page 32:

'Archibald Dickson of Hassendeanburn, his book 1745.'

So this accounts book for the nurseries had been begun by Archie's father, Robert, before he passed away in 1744. Then Archie had continued it until his death 50 years later. Chris recognised her husband's writing in ink listing the sales of trees, plants and seeds. She browsed through the pages until she came to the last 30, where she discovered accounts relating principally to sheep, cattle and agricultural work, as well as the terms of engagement with shepherds and farm servants. Also carefully noted were a number of entries dealing with money lent and repaid, bills paid and received.

Another smaller book lay on the table too. It was entitled 'Catalogue of herbaceous and ill bulbous-rooted flowers'. Archie had spent many a long evening entering all the details in his careful and methodical fashion. How he had loved order and she had loved him for that.

In it, she discovered a list of all the plants to be sold, all in perfect alphabetical order giving both the Linneas names as well as the English ones.

'Auriculas, fine sorts, named as mixture 2/6 to 4/6 each.'

At the back of this publication was printed:

'An extensive assistant of Foreign and Native Forest Fruit Trees, Greenhouse Plants, Garden Trees and Grass Seeds, Garden Utensils of All Sorts for which see other catalogues.'

And sure enough, in yet another catalogue, she found:

'Ash, aple trees, blackgeens, betches, chery trees, elam, fire trees, holeys, oak trees, plain, plum trees, labirnams, thorns, pees, beens, small beens, lintseed, cabitch plants, purtatoes, leeks, cabitch seeds, onions, leek seed, aples, gritt beens, wheet, wopen cole plants, bee skeps, hay, honey, beer, whin seed, hearbs turneep seed, persell seed, cress seed, pasneys seed, talaw, tarr, lickeras, musterd, lint, wax, oats, eggs.'

She could still picture Archie sitting in his chair in the office, spectacles on nose, making notes and writing letters of one kind or another. She turned back to continue reading, for it reminded her of those busy days long ago, and read:

'Three ews and lambs are sold to John Scott, herd in Eshebank at 7s per pear.'

'Robert Deans in Hassendean buys 3 stones of wool at 6s per stone; and William Rae pays 5s for the half of a stirk, which offer a contrast to present prices current.'

A list of customers then followed:

'The Duke of Argile, Markes of Lothian, Earl of Marchmont, Lords March, Drummond, Hyndford, Carnwarth and Minto, the Lairds of Galalaw, Todrig, Whitslade, Langlands.'

And on it went.

Chris recalled how he had so painstakingly but proudly made an entry noting the date and details of the trees sent to Windsor Great Park at the behest of the King's mother, Queen Caroline.

She then put down the book and picked up a third, this time entitled 'Farm Memoir Book and Servant's Ledger 1700-1774'. This seemed to consist of farm records, grain bought and sold, sheep bought and sold and similar entries, such as details of the servants' work and wages:

'16th May 1771. Archibald Thomson my servant to work in the nursery at Hawick, one year after Whitsunday, at five pounds twelve shillings sterling.'

'Thomas Grieve is hired to work in the nursery in Hawick one year at six pounds sterling of wages, and one stone of meal and sixpence each weak for meat.'

Children who were hired were also mentioned:

'Adam Cavers, haiered as prentice till Martinmas 1773. I am to give him sixteen shillings to buy shoon… And he is to go for four weaks to the school' and 'to have one month in the winter season to go to school.'

Chris closed the book, carefully put it back on the far table and then took off her spectacles. The business and the house had been left to Robert, her eldest son when Archie had died and he and his second wife, Catherine, had insisted on her staying on and living with them, just as Archie's mother had done in 1745. Chris was certainly not alone and everyone had been very attentive, but in spite of all the kindness bestowed on her, she still felt lonely without her Archie.

Of course, all of her other sons and daughters visited her regularly, bringing with them their spouses and children. Meg and her family in nearby Greenhouse came by daily bringing with them all the news of the day. Having lived through the time of the Jacobite Rebellion, the Seven Years War, the American War of Independence and now the skirmishes in France, Chris sighed and wondered if man would ever learn to live with his fellow man.

However local news was more heartening and folk roundabout were all talking about Selkirk's hero, Mungo Park, whom she and Archie had met while visiting their old friends, Dr and Mrs Anderson. Chris began to reminisce about the doctor for he had been a very hard-working and devout man, but one with a good sense of humour. She smiled as she recalled the tale often told of him about when, on going to the Sunday kirk service, he would bring a shilling and a penny with him and, when the plate went round he would put the shilling under the penny to hide it, being aware that most of the congregation could only afford a penny. Always well-respected for his dedication to his patients, she knew how he travelled miles on horseback in all kinds of weather over hills and through valleys to visit the sick, sometimes falling asleep on horseback. On returning home, he would then set about making up prescriptions and attending to accounts. Sometimes he would be called out again that same night, to visit the sick or to deliver a baby.

Then her mind went back to the Park lad, for Dr Anderson had been so proud when the young man gained his qualifications in surgery from Edinburgh University and then, with the help of his brother-in-law, James Dickson (no relation), had managed to get himself off to Africa to explore part of that unknown continent. Archie had been particularly interested in Park's expedition, as he had been sent by the Linnaean Society to discover new plants.

But of course the young explorer, being in Africa, had been unable to attend his older brother's June wedding in 1796, when Alexander had married pretty little Esther Turnbull, Chris's step-granddaughter. Although Esther lived in Roxburgh, she and Alexander had decided to hold the ceremony in Selkirk Parish Church, near to where he had been born and had grown up in Foulshiels. Chris had been invited to the celebration but had declined, as it was too far for her to travel. Had she attended, she would have known just about everyone at the wedding. However, she smiled as she remembered how she had been given a detailed account of it from her own 12-year-old granddaughter, Christy. The young girl had burst into her drawing room the following summer morning to tell her exactly what had happened.

"I've just spent the most glorious day of my life, Granny. Yesterday was like a piece of magic."

It transpired Christy and her older half-sister, Nelly, had stayed the night before the wedding at the Andersons' house in preparation for the next day and had met all their children. Sandy, the eldest, was a doctor and wanted to accompany his friend, Mungo, to Africa on his next expedition if there was to be one. Then came John, already a naval doctor, followed by the two girls, 15-year-old Allie and 13-year-old Bell, and then the twin brothers, Andrew and George, who were the same age as Christy herself. Finally came nine year-old Thomas,

"I truly like Allie and she told me a secret. Will you keep the secret if I tell you, Granny?"

Chris smiled and nodded, while wondering what she was about to hear.

"She plans to marry Mungo when he comes home. Isn't that exciting?"

Chris wondered if the young adventurer knew any of this plan, or perhaps the two already had an understanding. After all, Allie was growing into a very attractive young lady, or so she'd heard, and Mungo had always struck Chris as being a polite and affable young man. Of course at the time of the wedding he was in Africa exploring the River Niger, wherever that was. Ah well, rather him than me she thought, as she shuddered at the thought of the jungle. With that, she put a little prayer up to God to protect the young adventurer.

On the day of her granddaughter's visit, she had enquired about the rest of his family.

"So who exactly was there from this huge Park clan?"

"Well, Alex's mother was on her own, as Mr Park is dead. She was accompanied by all her sons and daughters, except Mungo of course. Even Alex's sister Margaret came, all the way from London with her husband. I think their surname is Dickson too. Are they relations of ours?"

"No lass, though he does come from the Borders – from near Peebles and he did work at Hassendeanburn as a young laddie. But then he went away to London and made a fair name for himself in Covent Garden. I mind it was through him Mungo was given the chance to go to Africa."

But her granddaughter had been less interested in Mungo's exploits than in recounting the previous day's events.

"Let me tell you about the day, Granny. After breakfast, the four of us, Nelly, Allie, Bel and I, got dressed in our bridesmaid gowns of pale blue embroidered silk. I felt truly elegant, Granny, with my laced neckline and lots of petticoats to make my skirts stand out. My hair was caught up with blue ribbons to match my dress and I wore matching silk shoes on my feet. Of course Esther, being the bride, had a veil to hide her face. She also held a bouquet of roses with a spray of white heather for luck."

Chris remembered how she had begun to feel drowsy, but Christy had prattled on.

"Then there was a knock on the door and two men were standing there ready to accompany us to the kirk, which is at the top of the High Street. Thank goodness it was June and the sun was shining, for we wore no hats or cloaks. I began to giggle because I thought the whole thing so funny, but then Nelly told me to behave like a lady and not a silly child. So for the rest of the day, I took everything very seriously. A piper led the way and we followed on behind Esther. Everyone was out in the street watching us and I felt very important."

"Once we got inside the kirk, Esther had to go to the front and kneel on a stool with Nelly standing by her side. Alex knelt beside her with his best man beside him. I don't remember his name. Then the minister gave a sermon and we sang your favourite 28th Psalm followed by the benediction – at least that's what Nelly called it."

"After the service, we went outside into the sunlight and, oh Granny, it was all so perfect. The minister kissed Esther, while Alex threw money to the waiting children. The crowd outside the church – there were lots of folk from the town – threw rose petals over the couple. That's what I want at my wedding."

"And I'm sure you will have it, lassie. So what happened next?"

Chris had tried to move her granddaughter on with the account, as she had been very keen to close her eyes.

"We then walked slowly up the High Street until we came to the Anderson's house where a meal was waiting for us outside. Thank goodness the weather was good, for there were so many people there the Anderson's house would not have been able to accommodate us all. The adults seemed to be drinking rather a lot – mostly the men – and toasting the bride and the groom.

Granny, some people I think were drunk and that's when all the singing began. That was a bit strange."

"An important part was the cutting of the wedding cake. It had two tiers, and Esther and Alex cut one. Did you know the other one is kept for the christening of the first child? That's what Allie told me. I didn't really enjoy my slice, as it had a funny taste. While it was full of fruit which I do like, Allie told me it was made of brandy. I was so glad when everything was cleared away and Esther and Alex got up to dance. They were such a handsome couple, Granny, and I'm sure their children will be good-looking too. Then they did a reel with us bridesmaids. I felt like a true lady in my bonny dress."

By the time Christy's account of the wedding had come to an end, Chris had closed her eyes and had fallen asleep as soon as the charming girl had taken her leave.

But all that had happened over two years before. So much had happened since then. A boy had been born to the couple the following year and was christened Mungo after his uncle. However, the lovely young Esther was not to see him grow up, for she died soon after his birth. Now, news had just arrived at Hassendeanburn House that Alexander was to marry again, this time to a lady called Alison Veitch. How quickly things changed.

Another little bit of news had also come to Chris that day. The Ayrshire poet, Robert Burns, had just published a song called 'Auld Lang Syne' and, always the performer, her granddaughter had sung it to her the day before. While Chris had listened to her granddaughter's rendition, she had noted the sentiment expressed in the song of the importance of friends and family. Now, as she lay in the warmth of her bed, she smiled and thought. Wouldn't it be grand to have the song sung at her funeral?

Part 2

Meg's Story

Chapter 1

1800: A New Century

"Should auld acquaintance be forget
   And never brought tae min'
   Should auld acquaintance be forget
   For auld lang syne."

"Well done, lass, that was truly grand." James proudly put his arm round his daughter, Christy.

Then from far in the distance, the toll of the bells from Minto Kirk could be heard through the mist and rain. They rang to welcome in not just a new year but a new century: 1800 had arrived.

Meg knew that in homes throughout the country people had been hard at work during the last few days 'redding the hoose'. Everywhere there was scrubbing of floors, polishing of brass, scouring of dishes, washing of clothes and cleaning of curtains. But she also knew that, at the stroke of midnight, all this work would stop for the celebrations would begin. In every house roundabout, be it in those of the families of farmers, weavers, souters, blacksmiths or nurserymen, the scene would be the same as in Greenhouse for everyone would be excited and ready to welcome in the New Year. The back door had already been opened to let out the old year and the front door open to welcome their 'first foot' who must be a tall, dark and handsome man, particularly not a red headed woman.

"A Happy New Year and health, wealth and happiness to one and all!" smiled James as he made his way towards the table in order to pour out the traditional 'wassail bowl' from its flagon. The warm spiced and sweetened ale containing an infusion of spirits was offered first to Meg and then passed to the other two women in the family, her 35-year old stepdaughter, Nelly, and her own 16-year old daughter, Christy. Little Meg at, only eight, was too young for such parties and was fast asleep in her bed upstairs. As head of the household, James would then top up the glass with another helping of whisky and hand it to his two young sons, 13-year old James, and 11-year old Archie. Adam, his eldest, was not with them for he was at his own farm at Hassendeanbank. James had passed him the tenancy on his marriage to Elizabeth Scott. That had been several years before and now they had seven children.

"Slainte."

The Gaelic toast known by all in Scotland echoed round the room.

Meg took the drink and while pursing her lips to imbibe the pungent spirit, she looked round at the members of her family. While her husband James, her stepdaughter, Nelly, and her three children James, Christy and Archie were there, her other stepdaughter, Nancy, was not for she was in Hawick with her husband. Meg was also reminded of some faces that were missing from the gathering that night – her own beloved mother being one. Chris had not quite made it into the new century, having died at Hassendeanburn only several months before. She had lived a long life, unlike Meg's first born James, who had died at only six.

Surely, however, the greatest and saddest loss to them all was that of her other stepdaughter, Esther, the beautiful young bride of only five years before. Meg could so easily picture her again on that joyful summer's morning in Selkirk when Esther and Alex had stood gazing into each other's eyes, surrounded by their many friends and family including the Dicksons, Parks and Andersons. She particularly recalled how much her daughter, the young Christy, had worshipped this attractive and vivacious older stepsister and how entranced she had been by the romance of the whole ceremony. But little did anyone know then that the jovial gaiety of that day was to turn to the cold bleak black of mourning only two years later when Esther died during the birth of her son, Mungo, christened after his uncle. Christy had been particularly inconsolable becoming even more so when Alex married someone else so soon after. She could not understand his actions and Meg sensed that her young daughter's zest for life had dimmed in spite of the happy news that her friend, Alice Anderson did marry the young explorer as she had planned when he returned to Selkirk, having been the first European to reach the River Niger in Africa. Yes, tonight was not only a time of celebration but also one of remembrance.

Now here was Christy dutifully handing round the shortbread, black bun in its heavy fruit and nut pastry case, and the 'carvie', the favourite caraway cake renowned for relieving a build-up of wind and generally easing any stomach pains.

Suddenly the door opened and in came their 'first foot.' Luckily, as custom decreed, the first person to step over the threshold was a dark haired man for there stood Adam, his dark hair and eyes shining in the candlelight, a piece of coal in one hand, a sum of money and a slice of cake in the other, while the traditional bottle of whisky was sticking out of his pocket. He had been in his own home at Hassendeanbank for midnight as was expected but, as soon as possible, he had made his way to join his father and family at Greenhouse. He was alone for his children were too young to accompany him – the oldest being only nine – and Betty, his wife, was expecting her eighth child sometime in the new year.

As the ale began to flow, the voices rose and the fun began.

After the greetings, kisses and welcoming drinks, Adam joined the group in trying to eat the 'snap-dragon'. This was a dish of raisins with brandy poured over them which was set alight for each person then to try and snatch a raisin without burning his fingers. On doing so the achiever had to make a wish. Young Archie was the first to do so and Meg watched with some amusement as he closed his eyes.

"Now don't tell us your wish, Archie," reminded his father, "for if you do it won't come to pass."

Meg smiled because she, like everyone else in the room that night, knew exactly what his wish would be. Archie, like all the children in the family, had grown up learning about plants, having been taught from an early age by their grandfather in his nurseries at nearby Hassendeanburn. Now that Meg's brother, William, had inherited the nursery in Perth from his uncle James, he had already offered this nephew of his a job there when he was older. Her son would become the fourth generation to work in the family business. The Hassendeanburn nurseries meanwhile were now run by Meg's oldest brother, Robert, who had knocked down the original family home there and instead built a very fine house overlooking the River Teviot. He would be there that night with his second wife, Margaret, his first Beatrix having died a few years earlier.

As for Meg's second brother, James, he would be with his wife, Christian, at Alton. He had been involved for many years with the British Linen Company and, although the Company's initial aim was to promote the linen industry on which the town of Hawick was heavily dependent, the Company had now moved on to banking and issuing its own notes. Having been accepted as a bank by the Royal Bank of Scotland, it now had agents throughout the country and James had been the second to be appointed.

Of her other brothers, Archie would be with Marion at Housebyres; William in Perth and Walter, her youngest brother, at Chatto or in Edinburgh. As for her sisters, she guessed Betty would be with Charles at Wauchhope; Janet with Alexander at Flatfield; Nancy with Walter at Whitmuirhall; and Christian with James in Hawick. These were the 10 siblings and they were all still alive.

The Turnbull family into which she had married, had not fared so well for James, her husband, had not only lost his own mother in his birth, his first wife, Agnes, his 27- year old daughter, Esther, and lately, his and Meg's own first born, James, who had died at just six. However, for all the tragedies James had had to face, he was still going strong at 64 and still working hard on his farm here at Greenhouse, no matter the weather. He had witnessed many changes in farming throughout the years and had just ordered a threshing machine for use on both his farms. Over the years, he had planted trees, as had her father and grand-father, thus helping to create new woods for both shelter and ornament and, above all, had been successful in breeding sheep, both Cheviots on the outfields and Beckwells on the infields.

Meanwhile, Meg had always been wise enough to know that, no matter how much James had been a kind and considerate partner to her, his first and greatest love would always be his beloved Agnes. She had known this from the beginning of their time together but she had accepted it and was glad to have been his helpmate throughout the years.

And now here was another of the Turnbull clan arriving at the door. It was her stepdaughter, Nancy, with her husband, William. Nelly, her sister, rushed across to see her, the two having always been close and had comforted one another when their younger sister Esther had died. Neither had children of their own but James would often joke that Adam, their brother, had made up for their lack of procreation by having already produced seven children and seemed to be in little hurry to call a halt to his ever-growing family. Perhaps, thought Meg, Adam needed to do so to compensate for all those in the Turnbull family now lying in their graves.

But it was Hogmanay and very soon William Graham,

Nancy's husband, took up his fiddle and Adam produced his penny whistle. In an instant the floor was cleared of tables and chairs, and soon everyone, both old and young, were up dancing a jig to the tune of 'Tulloch Gorum' to be followed by singing 'Hey Tuttie Taitie':

"Weel may we a' be,
Ill may we never see.
Here's to the king
And the gude companie."

The nineteenth century had certainly arrived. With its appearance Meg silently said goodbye to those left behind in the previous one, particularly to her own dear mother. How Chris Dickson would have enjoyed these celebrations. But she could not have lived forever and now it was Meg's turn to watch over the next generation.

Chapter 2

1802: A Visitor

"Meg, come away through and meet our visitor. Bring young Christy, if she's with you."

Meg did as her husband requested and, with their daughter, entered the parlour. In front of the fire stood James and beside him a tall, athletic and good looking young man with a mop of straw coloured hair half shielding a pair of twinkling eyes.

"George, allow me to introduce my goodwife, Mistress Turnbull, and our daughter, Christy, but I sense you two have already met."

"Of course we have, Father. George and I were at Esther's wedding in Selkirk and then we met again last year at Mungo and Allie's. George is Allie's brother, after all, Father."

The young man meanwhile bowed to both ladies while agreeing that a couple of meetings had already taken place.

"George has decided to become a farmer and so he's here to learn the ways of Greenhouse, as well as giving young James and me a hand."

"Welcome, lad, and we hope you will be happy here. You'll have a sup with us, I hope, before you begin? I'll have tea sent through. "

Meg took the young man's hand in hers and smiled up into

his open and friendly face. But James interrupted.

"No, no, woman. We're off for a dander round the farm. George has already been working on one nearby St Boswells, but he wants to learn all about sheep and their ways. Come you away, young lad, and find out. But, wife, could you redd up a room for the lad, he'll be biding with us? "

"Then we'll have a meal ready for you when you return at the end of your tour."

With that and another bow to both Meg and Christy, George followed James out of the door to join their son, James, who was already out in the fields.

"Ma, how can Father be so forgetful?" Christy exclaimed shaking her head and looking rather pink. "You've both known Dr and Mrs Anderson for years. He must remember George."

"Lassie, when there are all these young people about, he gets confused. I think he also finds it hard to connect with those in Selkirk after Esther's death there. You must remember he still has a grandson there, Esther's wee Mungo, but sadly he sees very little of him now that Alex has married again. "

"I knew all along that George was thinking of coming to see Father for Allie told me so when I saw her the other day in Peebles at her house in the Northgate. She was busy looking after their two bairns but she still had time to stop and tell me all the news. Ma, did you know that Mungo hates being a family doctor in Peebles so much that they are planning to go abroad to New South Wales – wherever that is? I'll miss them so much if they do move but it's pointless for them to stay if he's so miserable."

"But is he not still being entertained by all the great and good of London and Edinburgh society now he's written his book? Why does he want to go away again after having had such a time in Africa?"

"Allie says that, although he trained to be a surgeon and has now passed even more exams in London, his heart has never really been in helping the sick. His real interest has always been in botany and the study of plants. You should see the sketches he has drawn. They are lying all about the house and they're quite something."

"Well, I hope it all works out for them in the end. According to the gossip in Selkirk, the lad still suffers from terrible nightmares. Does Allie ever mention them? I'm surprised he's thinking of going back to another uncivilised world."

"New South Wales uncivilised? Where is it anyway?"

"I don't rightly ken, lass, but it's a long way from here."

"Well, Allie reckons he would rather face the dangers and diseases of the unknown, than go stravaiging over Scotland's moorland and mountains on horseback to tend to the sick. He also maintains Scottish doctors are badly paid here compared with those in England. That's what Allie tells me anyway. I know he did have a notion at one time of going back to the family farm in Foulshiels and helping out there but there were problems."

"Aye, his mother being one of them no doubt for she's a right busybody. That lad must really hate being a country doctor if he's saying that."

"Aye, his books may be a great success, but the job as a country doctor is not. The other Parks and the Andersons seem quite different. Allie says that not only is old Dr Anderson still wandering over the countryside attending to the sick as usual, but his children are following in his footsteps. Sandy, his oldest son – do you remember him? – is already a surgeon, and George's twin brother, Andrew, is another one and is at present preparing to join the army. Even Thomas, the youngest, has plans to be a surgeon. It's strange how George is firmly against such a career."

"Ah well, lassie, we're not all the same and I wish him luck with his ambitions in farming."

Meg smiled for it was not difficult to notice Christy's delight in having George at Greenhouse and she could not blame her daughter as he seemed such a likeable young man. Certainly Christy could do worse than marrying such a lad – and from such a well-liked and respected family too.

"You and he must be about the same age, are you not? I have vague memories of the twins being born about the same time as you appeared in the world. Am I right?"

"Aye he must be about 18 too."

"Oh well, you all grow up so quickly. Now I'm away to write to your Uncle William in Perth for Archie wants to visit Bellwood again.

Christy stopped thinking of their new guest and turned her thoughts to her younger brother.

"But, Ma, he's only 13!"

"Aye, but soon he'll be 15 and I know William will look after him well. He's certainly got the means to do so. That's what comes of being a bachelor – just like your other Uncle Walter in Leith. But enough of this prattle. We must go and think of a bite to eat. Our young visitor will need feeding up if he's to work here."

With that, Meg gave her daughter an understanding smile, took hold of her hand and pulled her towards the parlour door. Christy followed, a big grin of expectation on her face. Life was beginning to look considerably rosier.

Meanwhile outside in the yard, George went with the farmer to meet his 14-year old son, James, who was busy tending to one of the sheep. Although so young, he already seemed familiar with the ways of farming and of course Greenhouse would no doubt be his one day as his older half-brother Adam had already been given the tenancy of the Turnbull's other farm of Hassendeanbank.

To George, the Turnbulls seemed a complicated family what with this farmer having had two wives and two sets of children. George had never met the first wife as she had already died before he was born, but his parents had often spoken fondly of her and of his second wife too. How many times had he heard his mother say how much she admired Mistress Turnbull of Greenhouse for looking after her four stepchildren? He recalled that Adam was the oldest and only son from the first marriage but there had been three daughters, one being the ill-fated Esther. He also remembered hearing that Mistress Turnbull had lost a little boy in infancy. But her other four, Christy, James, Archie and Margaret, had lived.

Ah, yes, Christy. He well remembered playing with her at Esther's wedding when she had been a bridesmaid and had stayed the night with his family. Then she had been an annoying giggly girl but now she was an enticing, good looking young woman who would eventually be a catch for some lucky lad. He also remembered his mother once saying she looked like her grandmother, old Mrs Dickson from Hassendeanburn, who had been known to be quite a beauty in her day. But now, as Mr Turnbull had stopped and turned to him, George thought it wise to stop thinking about Christy and pay attention to what the old farmer was saying, or his training at Greenhouse might never take place.

"Now, lad, this is a medium-sized farm belonging to the Duke of Buccleugh but I have the tenancy. It has good arable land in the valley where we sow oats and barley and the land on the hills is good pasture land for the sheep and kye. Like abody else now, we've done away with the custom of having rigs as we had when I was a lad. Now everything's enclosed. We've also made great strides in farming since then, including grand improvements to the soil by what is known as 'shell marlin' or 'limin' always using manure. We have to drain the fields as well as level them and of course rotate the crops. You must already ken, lad, the great neep is sown to feed our beasts but I bet you didna ken it was introduced into these parts by the wife's father, old Airchie Dickson at Hassendeanburn. As for oats, they are auld Scotland's staple food providing us with our porridge and bannocks. But do you mind on two years past when the oats crop failed?"

George nodded and smiled. How could anyone on the country not have remembered the effect the failure had on everyday life?

"Well, thank the Lord, we still had the good old tattie to keep us going that year as well as the usual kale, peas and all the rest. Of course here at Greenhouse we aye have meat thanks to the kye – salted for winter days – and the usual lamb and chicken and sometimes James and Archie even bring home a puckle of salmon or trout from the river. And there is aye a good supply of eggs and daily produce so we shouldn't starve. We've even got our own beehives and the honey tastes right fine with the baking. "

George followed his guide around the farm while appreciating the pride in which the older man took in it. This farm was exactly what the young man had always dreamed of and so he listened carefully for any advice which would help him achieve his dreams.

"Of course it's not all about food. The sheep give wool for the spinners in Hawick to spin. Then it's dyed before given to the tailors to sew into the latest fashions and furbelows worn by the gentry in London and Edinburgh. As for the kye, they provide the leather for the souters in Selkirk to make into shoes. But, as a true Selkirk laddie, you'll know all about that already. But here at Greenhouse our interests are mainly centred on the wool which we sell to the factories in Hawick and around, to be made into hosiery or whatever. We're aye looking for improvements to the local breed so as to secure better yields in wool and carcass weight. At present we have many herds of pure Cheviots but we're aye experimenting with cross breeds, with sheep from the south o' the Border like Bakewells and Cowleys."

The two men stopped and stood in silence as they looked out across the fields to where the sheep were softly grazing. The only sounds to be heard were those of the birds twittering in the trees interspersed with the odd hammering made by the woodpecker. Everything seemed still except for the quick movements every now and again of the squirrels jumping down from branches and running after each other. Although having been brought up in a town, George was even more certain than ever that his future should be spent in this peaceful countryside, while running a farm like Greenhouse.

James turned to him and smiled: the guided tour was over.

"Now, I hope that gives you an idea of what takes place on the farm. Ony questions?"

Chapter 3

1806: An Invitation

"Mistress Turnbull, would you do Christy and me the honour of accompanying us to the Common Riding Fair tomorrow? I've got the day off and we thought you might like to see how we do it in Selkirk. Would you like to come?"

They were sitting round the kitchen table in Greenhouse having breakfast, the farmhands having already been out working for several hours. Meg smiled at Christy and George as they sat scoffing the usual porridge followed by bannocks and honey. Several months ago, George had asked James for Christy's hand in marriage and her father had readily given his approval. Meg and James had grown very fond of the young man over the couple of years he had been with them and he had worked hard to learn the ways of farming. When exactly the ceremony would take place was another matter, for first of all George must find his own farm.

Meg was struck by the kindness of the two young people for, despite their being deeply in love, they had still given some thought to her. She knew this was an effort to cheer her up, for life had been hard for all the family recently. Nelly, James's oldest daughter, as well as Margaret, their own youngest one, had both died of a fever. Meg had tended to them throughout but could do nothing to save them.

"Aye, Meg, you should go," agreed James. "I've got work to do and, if the weather continues to be like this you'll have a grand time. I mind on many a pleasant June day in Selkirk for the Common Riding and the sun aye seemed to be shining."

Meg went round to where the young lovers were sitting and put her arms round them both, smiled and nodded her acceptance.

"I'd love to come with you. I've never been to the celebrations in Selkirk before, as we always went to Hawick for their Common Riding Day. But I'm sure Selkirk will know how to do the ceremonies."

"Of course we do – and better!" George, being a true son of his town, smiled up at her with glee. "You can even have a bannock while you're there!"

The offer of tasting a bannock from Selkirk completed Meg's decision to accept the invitation, for the town was famous for its fruitcake and she had always been partial to a slice. Much as she had often attempted to make it herself and had paid great attention to the recipes given to her, she had never succeeded in making them to her satisfaction. As instructed, she had mixed the soft spongy dough of oatmeal and butter, added the buttermilk over many hours, and then added plenty of sultanas, finishing the top off with a glaze of milk and sugar before cooking it on a griddle. But it never turned out how she wanted them to. The offer to visit Selkirk and to sample the splendid bannock there urged her to accept the invitation.

"Thank you, young man, and I'm sure you'll have eaten several in your time. Now off you go back to work, George, while Christy and I get on with cooking your dinner."

After he had gone and while the two women were busy making broth, they discussed the Common Riding which had been celebrated for years in the Scottish Borders. Like all folk there, both had been brought up knowing about the festivities but Christy asked her mother to explain what they were really all about.

"Oh, I think it goes back to a long time ago, to when each burgh had its carefully guarded common land and, to keep it from any neighbours who might have wanted to steal it, stones were placed to mark the boundaries. Each year, the tradition was for the provost and the baillies to rig themselves up in formal dress, get on their horses and go down to inspect the stones. That's called the Riding of the Marches. The whole thing begins in the early morning and goes on all day. In fact, I think there is a whole week of celebrations of one kind or another. I mind dancing in Hawick at midnight to the 'Cornet's Reel Lass' when I was a lass."

"What's a cornet?"

"Oh, he's the standard bearer chosen from a number of young men. He has to be unmarried and an excellent rider. Now I think on it, it all stems from way back to the Battle of Flodden to honour all those who lost their lives that day."

Christy interrupted.

"That song 'The Flowers of the Forest' is all about that, is it not?"

"Exactly, lass. And did you know it was written by that strange old woman, Jean Elliot, whose family lived at Minto House and who was a neighbour of your grandparents? It is rumoured that she and her brother were travelling in the family coach one day and, being near Selkirk, they began to talk about the battle. He then wagered her a pair of gloves and a set of ribbons against her ability to write a good ballad on the subject. But she did just that – at least she wrote lyrics to an old piece of music. But later, however, she would never admit to being the author, although everyone around knew the truth. I remember her as a funny old crone. It was said that when she lived in Edinburgh, she was the only lady who went about in a sedan chair. She came back home only last year to die at her brother's house at Mount Teviot. Anyway let's get chopping."

Meg placed hunks of hen and bones together with the usual onions stuck with cloves, bouquet garni and herbs into the boiling water in the large black cauldron which was hanging on the see-hook over the fire. Then on went the lid and there the soup was left to simmer while she chopped the vegetables, soaked the barley and drained the peas to be added later. Meanwhile Christy, who loved baking, had taken out the griddle pan and was mixing the oatmeal, water, salt and butter to make oatcakes.

Although it was a fine day and the dish was really meant for the winter, Meg and Christy still prepared James's favourite 'stovies' from a recipe Meg's mother, Chris, had used at Hassendeanburn. Meg dropped a dollop of dripping into a thick-bottomed cast iron pan, while Christy added her chopped onions to fry. When ready, Meg topped the stew with tatties, covered it all with water and put the lid on the dish before placing it in the oven to cook in time for the workers to return.

The next morning, a fine Friday promising another warm day, everyone in Greenhouse was up and about early as usual. But for Meg, Christy and George, it was not to be a day of work but one of fun. Soon George was helping the two women into the trap to go to Selkirk, knowing full well there would already be crowds gathered in the town, events having already begun much earlier.

As they journeyed, George explained the procedure.

"At dawn, the standard bearer will have wakened the provost and dignitaries, and the band will have already accompanied them round the town. This is followed by An Act of Remembrance, when more music, including the usual 'Hail Smiling Morn' and 'Lead Kindly Light', will have been played. Then the crowds will have made their way round the West Port, the High Street, Back Row and the South Port. I mind all this because we lived in Back Row when I was a lad and we were always woken up with the music."

"Aye, that seems very similar to the goings on in Hawick."

"This is called the Casting of the Colours," whispered George, as a lone figure dressed as a soldier came forward carrying a flag. "He is representing the sole returner from the battlefield who carried that bloodied English flag of the Macclesfield regiment. 80 men were supposed to have set out from the burgh and only one returned. He was the bringer of the tragic news to the town."

Everyone watched as the standard bearer slowly lowered the ancient flag and then swirled it back and forth. The crowd stood in silence for a minute before the haunting refrain of 'The Flowers of the Forest' was heard played by a sole piper.

When the ceremony was over, Meg, Christy and George had time to speak to other friends and acquaintances before walking up the High Street to Back Row. This was a street long associated with the shoemaking trade and at the end stood the Andersons' house with its walled garden. Already George's mother was there at the door ready to welcome them.

"Come away, everyone. What a busy day it's been and, with such fine weather, the whole of Selkirk seems to have turned out to celebrate."

They followed Mrs Anderson into the parlour where a circular table was laid out for tea and with a very tempting, much awaited, bannock in pride of place.

"I'm so pleased you've come over to Selkirk, Mistress Turnbull. It seems so long since we've seen you and we were so sorry to hear of your losses. I know you will miss Nelly and your own little Margaret. But I hear James is getting on fine with the farm and his brother, Archie, is intending to join his uncle in Perth. Of course, above all, we are delighted with the news that the Turnbull and Anderson families will soon be joined, thanks to these two young people."

Mrs Anderson turned and looked affectionately at George and Christy.

"Yes, Master Turnbull and I are so pleased too. By the way, he sends his regards to you and Dr Anderson. How is the doctor? Is he around today?"

"He is, but he's in his surgery catching up on paperwork after the awful day he spent yesterday."

"Tell us about it."

"Well, he began visiting patients as usual stopping at Edinhope, 14 miles away, where he had breakfast. Then he went on to Dryhope and to St Mary's Loch, where Tibbie Shiel's son is seriously ill. After that, he rode on to the head of the Loch of the Lowes and over the high hills into Ettrick, visiting folk as he went, until he stopped for a tumblerful of toddy. While drinking that, a young lad was brought into the kitchen with his finger off, having caught it in the threshing mill. So my man got the poor lad sorted and finally made his way home, getting home around eight o'clock for a bite to eat. After that he was in the middle of making up the medicines to be delivered today, along with the prescriptions for those he had just seen, when he was called away to a midwifery case far up the Ale Water. So the accounts and letters had to wait until today, which he is attending to now. All this gallivanting is fine when you're young, but Dr Anderson is no longer that, so we're planning to retire to Broomhill when we can. Thomas, our youngest son, can carry on the work now that he's decided to be a country doctor too. But he's not yet finished his training in Edinburgh."

"And what of the others in the family? Any news of the two in Africa?"

"No, nothing yet. But we pray every day for their safe return. Meanwhile, I am visited daily by Allie full of complaints about Mungo's mother. You know she and the children have gone to live with old Mrs Park at Foulshiels and I don't think that can be too easy. Not that Allie was ever the most patient girl herself, but she has my sympathy. It must have been hard the way Mungo suddenly upped and left, telling her he was only going to Edinburgh for a few days, when in fact he and Sandy were on their way to Africa and had left that poor Walter Scott to convey the news to her. I am sure Mungo did it for all the right reasons. Perhaps he didn't want a tearful farewell. Anyway, I don't know whether she is heartbroken or furious, but I do know she misses him so much. The sooner he comes back to her and their four bairns the better. He'll have seen this River Niger and then hopefully he'll return and settle down. Sandy of course is away too and we miss him so much. He's such a gentle soul."

Meg could well understand it must be a difficult time for the Andersons and so she changed the subject to that of Mrs Anderson's other sons.

"And how are John and Andrew getting on?" Meg knew they were both surgeons in the military.

"John is now working back in this country with the Royal Marines in Woolwich, and dear old Andrew is stationed in Messina ready to confront the French. You should have seen what he had to buy to join the army! A long redcoat with black facing, a corded hat, a sword, gold epaulets, flannel shirts and boots, all of which cost him the better part of sixteen guineas. And they won't stay clean for long after he gets into the bloody job of operating. Talking of which, here's my husband now."

Mrs Anderson stood up and went towards the door. Meg noticed Dr Anderson was looking tired and slightly dishevelled. He quickly and absentmindedly bowed to Meg and Christy, bidding them welcome. He then turned to his wife, a piece of paper in his hand.

"Sit ye down, my dear, I have just received a letter from Africa. It's from Mungo."

Mrs Anderson sat down slowly, suspecting that the news was not good. Her husband then came over and sat beside her, arm around her shoulder.

"I'm afraid it's bad news, my dear."

Mrs Anderson's hand went to her mouth, while her eyes pleaded that it wasn't the news she had always been afraid of receiving.

"The letter is dated last year. My dear, our beloved son, Sandy, is no more. Mungo tells us that he died of a fever and dysentery in October by the banks of that River Niger."

Chapter 4

1811: An Arrival

So this was St Boswells again. Meg had never really liked the place, but it was here that George and Christy had accepted the tenancy of a farm nearby and had set up home. A few years before, they had spent one happy summer's day at the famous Fair there, wandering around the Green and visiting the many tents which displayed a profusion of goods for sale – linen dresses, aprons, tablecloths, wooden toys, crockery, leather shoes and books. They had taken a particular interest in the sheep, lambs, horses and hoofed cattle on show and by the end of the day they had decided to find a farm near there and set up home. Very soon they had found what they believed was the perfect place at nearby Camieston where George agreed with the laird, Captain Riddell Carr, to take up the tenancy.

But James's advice had been against his accepting this tenancy for several reasons. The land there was not as fertile as at Greenhouse and inclined to clay, and drainage was badly needed but lime, which was important to any farmer, would have to be brought in from afar, making it a costly business. Above all, James had also suspected George would have problems with Captain Riddell Carr for he, like many landowners, had plans to turn much of his land into grass for hunting purposes and, if this were to happen, George would find himself without employment.

However, despite his father-in-law's advice, George went ahead and he and Christy's wedding celebrations soon followed, taking place in this very church where Meg was now standing. That had been three years ago. Now here she was again with the rest of the family, but this time it was to welcome the second of their children, the first little girl having been born at Camieston the year before.

Life had turned out to be hard for them, as James had feared, with little money coming in and now here was another little mouth to feed. In spite of all these hardships, Meg knew, however, that the love between her daughter and George was enduring and that their affection for their children was apparent.

Christy was not, of course, there that day to witness the proceedings. The baby had been baptised Elizabeth Waugh Anderson after George's mother, their first-born having been called Margaret Dickson Anderson after Meg herself as was the custom.

As Meg sat watching the proceedings, she had time to rest and reflect. The world seemed in such an upheaval what with 'The Chronicle' each day publishing details of the war in France and elsewhere, for this Napoleon Bonaparte appeared to be trying to conquer the world. Certainly at first, many in Britain welcomed the French Revolution and supported the common people in their fight for liberty, equality, fraternity and the Rights of Man. However, when King Louis and his family were so cruelly guillotined, along with many other aristocrats, the Reign of Terror took hold and many supporters in Britain changed their minds.

As for the actual war with France, George was regularly receiving letters from his twin brother, Andrew, now a surgeon with the 79th Cameron Highlanders. Last year he had been in Lisbon with Sir Arthur Wellesley, then in Busaco, wherever that may be, but was now back in Spain. She recalled George reading one of these letters which described the loose women who were to be found around the camps and which concluded that they posed as much danger to the troops as death by a French cannonball. Meg shuddered to think what bloodshed and pain Andrew must be witnessing. This war seemed to have been going on for ages, and now it was 1811 and there still seemed to be no sign of its coming to an end. So far, Andrew seemed to have survived, but for others fate had not been so kind. Families throughout the land were receiving letters informing them of the deaths of their loved ones.

While the horror of war was being played out abroad, the hand of fate had also been cruel here at home. Meg looked at James beside her, now nearly 80, and marvelled at his stoicism. Not only had he lost three of his daughters but during the previous year, the greatest blow of all was to fall when Adam, his first-born son, had also passed away leaving Betty, his widow, alone to tend to their 12 children. Now not one of James' children from his first marriage had outlived him.

But the Turnbulls weren't the only ones to suffer loss. Meg looked across the pews to where George's family, the Andersons, sat. They too had witnessed one tragedy after another, beginning with the death of Sandy, their eldest, on that fatal expedition to Africa. Then they had to endure all those horrendous reports from London where their second son, John, had suffered a brain tumour and finally died. Meg had found the descriptions of the operations performed on him hard to listen to. Besides these two tragedies, the Andersons had also to endure receiving varying reports of the fate of Allie's husband, Mungo. Although it was almost certain he had been killed by natives or drowned in the River Niger, Allie would not accept his death and was still hoping that one day her husband would walk through the door again, just as he had done all those years before when he had returned from his first expedition.

Time had certainly been hard on the Andersons and, as if all this had not been bad enough, old Dr Anderson, so recently retired to Broomhill, had lost all his hard-earned savings as a result of the collapse of the bank in which he had invested his money. Now he and Mrs Anderson were living in Edinburgh, not to retire as planned, but to find another practice. Didn't he deserve to put his feet up? He couldn't go back to the Selkirk practice as his youngest son, Thomas, was now running it and, although there would no doubt be plenty of work to do, the funds were not there to pay for two doctors.

To complete the dismal series of events, Meg remembered that Thomas was now married to Margaret Scott of Deloraine, with whom Christy had fallen out for some reason. Meg suspected the cause had been jealousy on Christy's part for Meg knew her daughter's fiery temper and competitive streak. Was she ashamed of having a failing farm and a husband who would soon be looking for work, while Margaret had the social status of being a doctor's wife as well as having connections with the Scott and Sibbald families? Meg could well imagine Christy trying to hold her own by reminding Margaret Anderson of her own successful family connections and her wealthy landowning Dickson uncles. Dickson and Turnbull, her Uncle William's nursery in Perth, was expanding every year, having now over 50 people working on its 60 acre plantation. Archie, Meg's young son, was working there and turning out to be a very successful young man of business in Perth, while James, her other son, was ably running the farm at Greenhouse now that her husband had retired. Both young men were in their early 30s, both possessed caring hearts and happy dispositions which, Meg thought, was at least something to be thankful for

And so that day at St Boswell's Kirk, the Dickson, Turnbull, Anderson and Park families had congregated and, as they rose to sing the next hymn, Meg wondered what the future held for them all. The land had certainly been good to the Dicksons and the Turnbulls, but time was moving on. More and more people everywhere were leaving to try their luck in towns and cities. Factories were opening up, the iron and steel industries were beginning to develop because of the invention of the railways,

"It may be, but we in Selkirk have a special ceremony that only belongs to us souters."

"Oh, and what's that, may I ask?" enquired Meg.

"You'll just have to wait and see. Oh, and by the way, my mother's invited us to tea after the ceremony. You and she always seem to enjoy a good chinwag when you get the chance, am I right?"

Meg smiled and nodded in agreement.

"How kind, I'll really enjoy that. I'm sure she'll have much to tell us about your family and what you Andersons are getting up to. Your brothers seem to be getting on so well with their medical careers."

Meg instantly wished she hadn't added the last remark as it might have been seen as a criticism of George. However, he didn't seem to be offended so she continued.

"And as for the bold explorer, have they heard anything about how his second trip is going?"

"No, nothing. You know my older brother, Sandy, is also with Mungo in Africa and I often wonder how he's getting on. Unlike Mungo, all sport and fitness, Sandy is rather puny. But maybe he'll prove me wrong and be able to cope with the jungle. You wouldn't get me out there is all I know. I've no desire to come across these tribes of strange people, not to mention the animals and insects they'll no doubt be encountering"

"Or coping with the heat and disease," added Christy. "But let's forget about them and enjoy the day here. Look, Ma, there's old Mrs Mercer and is that not Mrs Hogg beside her?"

"It is indeed. This is going to be a grand day, I can feel it in my bones, lass."

Soon they had descended from the trap, while George took the horse and tied it up nearby. Then Christy and Meg went over to greet their friends before making their way to the marketplace to find a spot in the crowd from which to view the ceremony. Soon the provost and the magistrates, dressed in their robes and chains, came down the High Street, spearmen on either side of them to the place where the next event was about to happen.

and ship building was calling for more workers. Sadly, many in the Highlands had already left their native Scotland, having been driven out to make way for sheep and had sailed to the New World.

She also suspected George and Christy would not be staying much longer in Camieston: that they would be forced to leave the peace and security of the countryside and head for the city. Meg fervently hoped they would not be tempted, as were many, to cross the Atlantic to seek their fortunes. However, anything was possible in such unsettling times.

Chapter 5

1815: A Confession

The firelight flickered on the parlour walls. The crackle of the burning wood and the ticking of the clock in the corner was all she could hear. It was late. Meg always cherished this time of night, sitting beside the warmth and peace of her own fireside. Many a night she had sat with James sometimes reading, sometimes sleeping, but more often talking, either planning the next day or reflecting on life in general. She had always enjoyed listening to him especially when he had recited the words of his beloved Burns' poems, 'A Cottar's Saturday Night'. There was one verse in particular which had appealed to him. How did it go again? Meg thought for a moment and then the lines came to her.

"From scenes like these, old Scotia's grandeur springs,
That makes her loved at home, revered abroad:
Princes and lords are but the breath of kings,
An honest man's the noblest work of God."

James had delivered these words with such pride and such emotion. However, he was no longer with her, having died the previous summer, just missing the end of the long wars in Europe which had been part of their lives for so long. She and James had married only five years before the French Revolution and it had taken all that time to bring it to an end with the Battle of Waterloo. At last, the Emperor Napoleon had been banished for good and, according to the newspapers, a king would soon be on the throne of France once more. What was it all about? The wars had cost Britain dear, leaving many a household grieving a husband, son or father who had lost their lives in the conflict.

Because of James' passing, their son James had inherited Greenhouse and there she was now living with him. He was still without a wife. She missed James more than she would care to admit but, when she looked up on that particular evening, she saw another figure sitting in James' favourite chair. It was George, her son-in-law. Christy had long since retired to bed and their children were tucked up in theirs. How time marched on, she thought. One minute she had been accompanying the young pair to the fair in Selkirk, and the next, they were a married couple with four children – Margaret, called after her, was six; her little sister, Elizabeth, after George's mother, four; John, after George's brother, three; and little James, after Christy's father, two. How the family had grown in these seven years of marriage. They were still a loving family but that night, as Meg looked across at George who sat gazing into the firelight, he appeared to have all the cares of the world heaped on his hunched up shoulders, his face tightly drawn as if in deep troublesome thought.

"What is it, lad? What ails you?" she whispered. Nothing stirred. No answer came. It was as if she had never spoken. Then after a deep intake of breath, George put his head in his hands and spoke.

"I'm an utter failure. I have achieved nothing. All my brothers and brothers-in-law have become successful and prosperous. Even though Mungo is dead, he is revered. I can't even go down the street without someone asking if I'm related to him. He's now become a national hero and everyone seems to be reading his books. Then there are my brothers. Andrew has returned home from the wars a hero, having cared for the soldiers throughout the campaign in France, Italy, Portugal, the Netherlands or wherever else he has travelled. Even little Thomas is now a doctor running the practice in Selkirk and rapidly growing into a well-liked and well-respected family doctor throughout the parish. As for my brothers-in-law, your sons, you just have to look at the wonderful work Archie is doing in Perth and James back here in Greenhouse. That is more than can be said of my attempts over at Camieston. That was a complete disaster and now here we are with you. I have no job, no training and no prospects, but I have a wife and four children to feed."

"But do remember, lad, all those you have mentioned have had doors opened for them by friends and families. They have inherited businesses, property and medical practices. Some have also been helped by being introduced to people of influence. Take Mungo. Would he ever have achieved his chance to journey abroad without his brother-in-law's introducing him to the right people in London? Would your brother Andrew have got his commission in the army so easily if it hadn't been for his older brother John's connections? Would Archie have been given the opportunity of being part of such a nursery as Bellwood if it hadn't been that it belonged to his Uncle William? Would Thomas have got the practice in Selkirk so easily had your father not decided to retire? As for James here, would he have found himself in charge of such a well-run and successful farm had it not been left to him by his father? You came from a medical family with no connections in farming, lad. Besides, you took on a very difficult tenancy with a difficult laird who didn't do much to help you. Now it is more difficult to find work on the land, as you have found out to your cost. Cities are now where the work is and while of course I don't want you and Christy to leave here, the old order is changing and I suppose we must accept that, whether we like it or not, if we are to survive."

"But I must be such a disappointment to you. Surely you must have wished for something better for your daughter and grandchildren."

"I have never been disappointed in her choice, George. Never. And I never shall."

Then they both sat for a few minutes in comfortable silence, wrapped in their own thoughts, deep in contemplation. Meg thought back to her own choice of life when she agreed to marry James all those years ago. The farm had been successful enough but, on reflecting how things had turned out, she realised she must have been regarded by other members of the family as the poor relation, for most of her five brothers were now or had been lairds and owners of estates. James, now dead, of Alton; Robert, now also dead, of Huntlaw; Archibald of Housebyres; William of Bellwood and Walter of Chatto.

As for her sisters, the eldest, Janet, was living at Flatfield with her husband, Alec Clark; Agnes at Whitmuirhall had been married to Walter Dunlop but was now a widow; Elizabeth at Wauchope had been married to Charles Scott but was also a widow; while Christian, her youngest sister, was living in Hawick still married to the Rev. James Henderson. All, except herself, had taken a step up in the world both socially and financially.

While she had enjoyed visiting their fine mansions, marvelling at their clothes and delighting in travelling in their splendid coaches, she had never truly envied them. There had been one thing, however, nothing to do with financial wealth, that she had craved, and one thing she doubted if any of her sisters truly possessed. She had never admitted it to anyone but now, after all these years, she found herself doing so to her son-in-law.

"George, I've never told this to anyone before so listen carefully to what I am about to say. I know how blessed I have been throughout my life and I know there is more to life than material wealth. But there was something I never really did possess and it is something you and Christy share. James was a kind and caring man who supported me through the highs and the lows of life. He was an interesting companion and for that I would never have changed him. However, I always knew that in his heart I was always only a poor second best, for his real passionate love was for Agnes. No one would ever have truly replaced her in his affections. But then I suppose I always knew that from the start. Yes, I know he was infinitely grateful to me for looking after and caring for his children, but we never shared what you and Christy feel for each other. You should always cherish that and thank the good Lord for bringing you together."

Meg sat very still, almost startled at herself for disclosing such a confession, and to her young son-in-law of all people. But slowly George turned his head towards her, looked into her eyes and smiled. He understood. Then he stretched out his hand and taking hers in his, he gently squeezed it.

"Thank you for sharing that with me. I am honoured to have been the one to hear it. Christy always suspected that that was so between you two. She and I do know how lucky we are in our love for each other and how blessed we are in having such great bairns."

He nodded his head and smiled. This time he had a twinkle in his eye.

"In fact, now I must share something with you. Next year you are to be a grandmother again."

"That's the best news I've had in ages. You realise that if it hadn't been for you two I would never have had any grand-children at all, for it doesn't look like either James or Archie are interested in settling down with a wife and family. Of course I am a grandmother to Adam's brood, but they have moved away with their mother now that Adam has died and I don't see much of them. My dear, I'm so happy and so proud."

Neither of them was aware that another person had entered the room. Christy, in long white night gown and Paisley-pat-terned shawl round her shoulders, came quietly towards them, lit by the candle she was holding.

"What have you two been talking about so late into the night? I woke up and you were not by my side, my love. I missed you."

As she spoke, she knelt by George's feet and, putting one hand on his knee, rested her head in his lap. He gently touched her head and began stroking her golden curls.

"Ah, that would be telling. But I have just told Ma about the new baby."

"Yes he has, my dear, and I'm delighted. You keep building up your fine family as it gives me great joy in my old age. And you know you are all welcome to stay here at Greenhouse for as long as you wish. James enjoys your company and appreciates the hard work you do, George. As for me, I love being surrounded by the energy and fun of young people. Life is never dull when you're around."

As the clock in the corner struck midnight she added, "But now I think it's time for bed."

George took Christy's hand and helped her to her feet. Then he turned and, taking Meg's hand, drew them both to him giving them a big hug. As they made their way to the door, George turned to Meg and said in his low and comforting voice, "Thank you for your words of wisdom tonight. We all love you, you know."

Before climbing into her large high bed with its familiar white crocheted cover, Meg clutched one of its brass knobs and carefully lowered herself down on to her knees. Every night as always, no matter how late the time or how tired she was, she had said her prayers since childhood. Tonight was no exception. She clasped her hands in front of her, closed her eyes and quietly asked God to look after this young Anderson family. Her life on earth was slowly coming to a close, but she prayed that He would keep this family safe and that the love Christy and George had for each other now would last throughout their lives.

Part 3

Christy's Story

Chapter 1

1818: A Journey

"Come away in, Christy. I've just received some good news. I see George isn't with you but I know he's got work to do. You'll have to convey the news to him yourself."

Christy followed her sister-in-law into the parlour at the Dovecote. Past animosities between the two women were now long forgotten, and now Margaret appeared to be almost bursting with excitement which greatly amused Christy. What was this news? She had to wait until she had been settled in a chair with a cup of tea and a scone before she found out. Even then, she had to exchange the usual pleasantries before doing so. Margaret first enquired about Christy's family back at Greenhouse where they were living with her mother and brother.

"How are the bairns? I haven't seen the boys for ages. How old are they now?"

"John is seven and attending school with Margaret and Betsy, while James, only five, is still at home with our little Christina. Ma is very good at helping me out with the children and is just now looking after the two youngest ones."

Christy was indeed grateful for her mother's support in more ways than one, for George was now working on the farm at

Greenhouse as ploughman. His brother-in-law had replaced the old Scots plough with one driven by a team of one man and two horses and these animals needed tending from early morning until evening. George, having always been good with horses, not only ploughed but tended to all the horses on the farm, as well as those used for transport. Meanwhile Christy had taken on the role of housekeeper and she and her mother worked together to look after the house and the children. Christy often wondered where her family would have been without the help of Meg.

"And what about your brood, Margaret?"

The answer was accompanied by her sister-in-law's collapse into a nearby chair.

"I'm exhausted with these three scamps running around all over the place although they're also at school at present. Poor wee Agnes is upstairs in bed and is still ailing. And now here comes the latest addition."

Margaret turned towards the open doorway where stood Bel the nurse with a tiny baby in her arms. She had been with the family ever since Thomas and Margaret had wed and had attended to all the children. Now here was John, sleeping soundly in his blanket cocoon. No doubt he had been christened after John, their brother-in-law who had died so tragically of a brain tumour in London quite some years before. Christy and George had also named a son after him. Names were so often duplicated in families and this would no doubt not be the last in the two Anderson families. So far, there hadn't been a Margaret, Elizabeth or Christian at Dovecote as at Greenhouse, but then there was still plenty of time for that to happen.

Christy carefully took her baby nephew from Bel's arms and delighted in the smell of the newborn infant, who seemed oblivious to all that was going on around. Christy smiled to herself. Why did babies of this age always look like old men with their often bald heads and red, crinkly faces? What would become of this little John she wondered? She bent over him and placed a gentle kiss on his forehead before handing him back to his nurse.

"Anyway, Margaret, enough talk of the children. What is this news you are holding back?"

Margret took one last sip of tea from her cup, then put it down in the saucer and sat back with a big smile on her face.

"Andrew is to be married."

"What? When? Where? Who's the lucky girl? Do we know her?"

Christy clapped her hands together with joy. This marriage of George's twin brother had been a long time in coming. Andrew had always written home regularly over the years from the time he first joined the army as an assistant surgeon working in Sicily, and then as a full surgeon stationed at Flushing, Burgos and Salamanca during the sieges there. But during all these years there had never been any mention of a young lady.

"George will be delighted to hear the news."

"Yes, at last. You remember, when Andrew was abroad, he was always writing to us saying how much he would like to be back at home sitting by his own fireside instead of facing the boredom and dangers of war?"

"I do."

"Well, now he's become a full doctor he has found himself a wife and should be able to fulfil his wish in great comfort."

Christy was reminded that her brother-in-law, after returning from the end of the war, had gone back to university to study for three more years in order to become a fully qualified doctor. Presumably because both he and Margaret's husband, Thomas, were both doctors, Andrew had communicated more with him than with his twin, George. This Christy knew had always been a bit of a disappointment to George, but then he had to accept that he was not one of the medical fraternity. Anyway, it was good news and she was pleased for her brother-in-law.

"I know Andrew is in Ireland at present but do tell me when

or where he met his intended. More importantly, Margaret, who is she?"

"Do you remember Mungo and Allie talking about a lawyer in Peebles by the name of James Cairns? His wife was called Isabel. No? Well anyway, it's their daughter, Anne, who is the lucky girl. I think she met Andrew in Edinburgh at one of these army balls and they are to be married this very August in Portpatrick in Wigtownshire."

"Why Portpatrick?"

"I've no idea but, presuming we'll be invited to the wedding, we better make a visit to Edinburgh soon and arrange our outfits. Do you fancy taking a trip into town next week, as we've only a couple of months to go before the big event?"

Christy swallowed at the thought of the expense, but then decided it would be worth it. After all, it wasn't every day that George's twin brother got married, and so she agreed.

"We could visit those new shops in Princes Street. We need not go near the High Street now with its crowds, stinks and pickpockets. Let's explore the New Town."

"I do so agree. And I believe those new shops are worth seeing, for they are displaying all the latest London fashions. I haven't visited Edinburgh for such a long time and I hear those new houses in those elegant squares are quite grand. And the gentry living there are even grander with their fine clothes and smart coaches, not to mention the spectacular livery of their servants."

Christy's eyes shone in expectation of the visit.

"It must be so different from the Old Town. You never knew what was happening up those closes, and the chance of being pelted with the contents of a chamber pot from above is not my idea of fun."

Margaret giggled in agreement.

"Nor mine. So that's a date. We'll look as good as any of those high and mighty ladies."

With that Margaret struck a pose and dangled an imaginary fan in her hand. Christy laughed at Margaret's antics and stood up.

"Now I must depart and give George the news. Is Andrew coming home soon from Ireland?"

"I expect so and I hope we shall soon be introduced to his intended. Oh, what fun!"

The two ladies almost reverted to the young lassies of yesteryear as they half-danced their way to the door, giggling as they went.

As expected, Andrew did return home soon after and did introduce everyone to Anne. The family all approved of her, finding her to be a most charming and intelligent young lady. Everyone was delighted that at last Andrew had found a wife with whom he could settle down and raise a family of his own, wherever they were to live.

Spring soon turned to summer and on a sunny day in August, the various members of the families made their way to the church in Portpatrick to witness this long-awaited wedding. Afterwards, they toasted the newly-married couple and wished them all happiness in their future life together.

All too soon, it was time for Andrew and Anne to leave Scotland and return to Ireland where Andrew was based. However, they were not to be staying long at Castlebar, for the regiment was about to be sent to Jamaica the following spring. Anne wrote regularly to her sister Cath in Peebles, always expressing her excitement over the journey to the West Indies, at the same time sharing her fear of being seasick. Cath would then visit Selkirk and Greenhouse and relay such contents of her sister's letters to Christy and Margaret.

In one such letter Anne had written, "I am going, it is true, far, far from friends and home, to sojourn in a foreign land; but wherever I go, the remembrance of that home will cheer me and be the subject of many a thought and conversation. My mother, I am sure, will be sorry and uneasy at the thought of it, but God who watches over me here will protect me elsewhere, and will never forsake those who trust sincerely in Him."

Anne had always been very keen on drawing, painting and sewing since girlhood and so fretted over the art materials she would take with her on her journey. Finally, she decided on some good drawing paper, varnish, white velvet, silk and thread. She was also planning to make tippets to go with a spencer she had already made, although knowing full well she was unlikely ever to wear it in the heat of Jamaica. Sometimes she wrote of her worries concerning what to take with her and what to leave behind. Although advice was being given to her by other officers' wives, no one really knew much about Jamaica other than it would be very much warmer than Scotland. She also planned to learn Spanish, knowing Andrew was already fluent in the language.

Allie Park, her sister-in-law, also received long letters from her, and in one letter Anne admitted she suspected Andrew would rather have been staying in Scotland in Shawwood, his own house which he had inherited from his brother, John, than embarking on the journey. However, it was too late to change their minds and so on the 16th April Andrew and Anne left Cork and made their journey to the West Indies, knowing they would probably be staying in Jamaica for at least three or four years.

Two months later, the families back in Scotland received word that, after their long journey, the couple had eventually arrived at Up Park Camp, Jamaica. Anne described the journey as her being the only lady aboard their ship in which they had sailed, along with twelve officers, and admitted to having been seasick as she had feared. Nevertheless, the weather had been beautiful during the sail and the ocean calm. She wrote that she had been happy with the accommodation aboard, for she and Andrew had been given a neat small cabin big enough for a bed and their entire luggage. There had been three ships sailing together and, during some evenings, the band on their boat played tunes for the three vessels to enjoy. Anne had been particularly excited when she had seen the peak of Tenerife as they passed, a very grand sight seldom seen from the sea. On her arrival in Jamaica she then wrote of the welcome they received, when it seemed that the entire population of Kingston had crowded in to see the novel sight of the Highland regiment.

By August, Anne had pleasing news to share with those back home. She had given birth to a little girl and, although she herself had not been well after the birth, declared the baby to be a pretty healthy little infant. Soon, however, the proud young mother was better again and wanting to call the child Isabel after her mother, while the proud father, Andrew, had other ideas. As the little girl had been born on Napoleon's birthday, he thought the name Josephine would be fitting but if not, Elizabeth, after his mother. However, Anne did not care for either of these names.

But more pressing events took place. In the middle of all this happiness and excitement, the little family found themselves surrounded by death. Within two months of arriving, the most virulent strain of yellow fever had spread throughout the regiment and 140 men, three officers and thirteen women as well as the same number of children were lost to the disease.

One month after Andrew's letter arrived describing the awful consequences of the deadly disease, the families were to receive another one, again from Andrew. He explained how he himself had caught the fever, having looked after all the dead and dying, and had returned home one night unwell. After three days of being looked after so tenderly by Anne, he began to recover, but by then she had begun to feel unwell. He arranged for her to go to the hospital in Kingston but sadly, after only four days of contracting the fever, she died.

All the relatives back in Scotland were shocked. They could not believe that, after so much happiness, tragedy had struck in so short a time. It had been just over a year since they had celebrated the wedding in Wigtownshire. Now the young bride was lying buried in the Church of England cemetery in Kingston, leaving behind a grieving husband and baby girl, barely two weeks old.

In the end the child had been christened neither Josephine, nor Isobel, nor indeed Elizabeth for, in memory of her dead mother, she was christened Anne.

Chapter 2

1822: A Farewell

Christy stood at the front door of Greenhouse and looked around. She took a moment to appreciate the warmth and peace of her surroundings, broken only by the clucking of the hens as they busily pecked at the grain on the ground nearby and the bleating of the sheep in the distant fields. Her eyes then lifted to the faraway pastures studded with white woolly blobs of sheep, standing out against a background of gently undulating hills of green and purple.

Today all was tranquil, but Christy could remember, as well as the blissful balmy days of summer, many harsh days of winter when the biting winds blew across the bleak and stark landscape. She had grown up here in Roxburgh. This was her home. This countryside and farm life was all she had ever known.

But it was time to say goodbye to the Borders and to the countryside for, like many country folk, they were about to make their way to the towns and cities to find work. In the nearby town of Hawick, for example, while many women were still spinning and weaving at home, mills had sprung up and the town was steadily growing as were other Border towns. Some folk had gone to the main cities of Edinburgh and Glasgow, while others had gone even further afield to make new lives for themselves in America or Canada, causing them to say goodbye forever to their folks left back home in Scotland.

Now it was the turn of Christy's family to bid farewell to the countryside and all they had known. Although her mother and her younger brother had very kindly taken them in to live at Greenhouse, James could no longer promise that Greenhouse could support so many mouths to feed, for over the years the Anderson family had grown. Now George and Christy had six children, Margaret, Betsy, John, James, Janet and Christy and another wean was on the way.

George and Christy had often sat round the fire with James and Meg trying to solve the work problem. George had found temporary work in Edinburgh in the docks at Leith, only coming back to Greenhouse at weekends to visit his family. He found the city uninviting with its division between the filth and degradation of the Old Town and the splendours and delights of the New. He was aware his family would never be able to live in a fine house in the city's west end and were more likely to find themselves living in the poverty round Leith Walk, so Edinburgh held no attraction. But what was to be done?

Then one evening, when George was over in Selkirk visiting Thomas, his younger brother, he met John Scott, an old school pal who had just returned from Glasgow. He described what was taking place along the River Clyde, where four of the five main ports in Scotland were to be found. He enthused about the opportunities there, particularly in a town called Greenock, 22 miles from Glasgow, where a most impressive and vast customs house had been built only four years before. Scott described the elegance and style of the palatial building with its Grecian pillars facing its newly formed docks on the River Clyde. These docks could hold 500 sailing ships, most of which were owned by wealthy Glasgow merchants. They came in from across the world bringing rum and sugar from the West Indies, tobacco, mahogany and cotton from the Americas, timber, iron and hemp from the

Baltic, and wine and fruit from Spain and Portugal. New houses, coffee houses and shops were springing up daily because of this industry and now Greenock had become the fifth largest town in the country. John strongly advised George to consider making his future there.

And so it came to be. George sought employment in the town and soon found himself working in this impressive Greenock customs house as a land-waiter – a customs officer – a job with which he was already familiar, having been employed as such in Leith. He was to oversee the landing of goods and had the responsibility of examining, tasting, weighing, measuring and accounting for the merchandise that landed.

He knew he could manage the job and would enjoy the work and so, not long after, he found a home for his family in Patrick Street, in Port Glasgow, only a few miles away from Greenock. Dates were fixed, travel was arranged, and soon all the packing was done.

The Saturday before their departure, a farewell party had been held at Greenhouse to say goodbye to the family, and Christy had been touched to see that some of her old uncles and aunts had made the effort to attend. Uncle Archie from Housebyres, now approaching 70, was there with his wife Aunt Marion and their children, Walter, James and Marion. Her Uncle Walter from Edinburgh and Uncle William from Perth were absent, now being too old and too frail to attend and Christy's two other uncles, Robert and James, were dead. However, some of their children from Hassendeanburn and Alton had come to say farewell, as did Aunt Elizabeth from Heuchleuch with her eldest son, Archie, now Laird of Wauchope, plus two of her younger children, Rachel and George. Old Aunt Agnes from Whitmuirhall, aged 86, was missing but her sons, Christy's cousins, Charles and Walter were there too, as were her Aunt Janet from Flatfield and Aunt Christy and Uncle James from Hawick.

Christy had particularly rejoiced to see that her brother Archie had made the effort to come all the way from Perth to be with them that day, and it was good to see him looking so well and so happy. She promised she would visit him and their old Uncle William in 'the Fair City' one day. Archie was still unmarried and it looked as if he would follow in the footsteps of both his bachelor uncles, William and Walter, and dedicate his life to his plants. However, he was still only 33 so anything could happen yet.

As for George's relations, his younger brother, Thomas, came with Margaret and their boys, Alexander, Henry Scott, Thomas and John from Selkirk. They were perhaps of all their relations the ones to whom George and Christy were closest for, although George was two years older than Thomas, both couples had been married and had children around the same time. Now, both Margaret and Christy were once again pregnant. Christy knew Margaret was hoping for a girl this time and one who would survive for both her daughters, Agnes and Elizabeth, had died in infancy. Andrew, George's twin, was disappointingly not able to be there. He was still in Jamaica but thankfully still alive, despite the awful conditions which had killed his wife. However, George's younger sister, the lovely 22-year-old Isabella, was there accompanied by a little five-year-old girl who turned out to be none other than Andrew's daughter, the little Anne. She had been sent home from Jamaica as soon as her mother had died and was now living with her aunt in Peebles. Christy had rarely met the dainty little thing, but now was so pleased to see her playing happily with Christy's own daughters.

As for George's other sister, Allie Park, now staying in Clare-mont Street, Edinburgh, with her four children, although fully intending to come, did not in the end manage to do so for Mungo, her eldest son, now a qualified surgeon, was getting ready to go to Madras and she needed to help him get ready.

Now it was time to say goodbye. All was packed and ready to go, and James was in the process of bringing the pony and trap round to the front of the house. First they were to make their way to Hawick, from where they would travel by coach to

Glasgow and then on to Greenock, stopping for several nights at various inns on the way.

So this was to be one family which would not be going to Edinburgh that day, despite the long-awaited arrival there of King George. For weeks all the newspapers had been full of the details of the monarch's visit. It had largely been organised by Walter Scott from Abbotsford, now a successful writer of novels. Margaret, Christy's sister-in-law, had just informed her that Scott's new book was entitled 'The Pirate', in which there were two characters supposed to be based on her and her sister. Even George was reading Scott's newest work, 'Ivanhoe', but whether he was enjoying it, Christy was unable to tell. It had been so long ago since Scott and his brother-in-law, Mungo, had been friends.

Christy meanwhile would carry on reading her own favourite novel, 'Pride and Prejudice', and was struck by the opening lines delivered by Mrs Bennett:

'It is a truth, universally acknowledged, that a single man in possession of a good fortune must be in want of a wife'.

Throughout the book, poor Mrs Bennett had spent her time trying to find suitable husbands for her daughters. Then it dawned on Christy that that might well become her role in life in the future. Would she be dedicated to the pursuit of suitable husbands for her four, perhaps five, daughters?

She dismissed the thought on hearing footsteps behind her and, on turning round, she saw Meg, her eldest at 13, holding the little one-year-old Janet in her arms. Christy recalled herself at that age, when she had been bridesmaid to her older step-sister, Esther, so long ago. That was nearly 25 years ago, she calculated, and yet she could still recollect her excitement. But Esther, of course, was now long dead and her son, Mungo, was now a young man.

Meg was soon joined by her sisters, the 11-year-old Betsy and six-year-old Christina. What a picture the four girls made. All of them had been born here in the Borders but this new addition to the family, soon to arrive any day, would make its way into the world of Greenock. Would it be another girl? Yes, Christy could well see herself in a few years' time becoming another Mrs Bennett.

Betsy approached her mother.

"Ma, Granny says that she can't find the boys. Have you seen them? She says she hopes they're still clean because they've got on their best clothes and they'll have no time to change now if they've mucked themselves up."

"Betsy, you and Christina go and look and leave Meg to look after wee Janet. Oh and fetch Granny too because I can hear the trap coming."

Soon all the children were rounded up and standing by her side looking more or less respectable. The valises were on board and finally it was time to kiss her dear mother goodbye. The old lady had been such a support to Christy and her family, and now here she was at 72 bustling busily around bidding them all farewell, while promising to visit them soon in Greenock. Perhaps she would do so, but Christy very much doubted it for the journey would be too long for this grand old mother of hers.

George also bade Meg a fond goodbye and then turned to his family.

"All aboard, everyone. We'll have to leave now if we're to catch the coach for Glasgow."

"Aye, George, we're all ready." Christy turned to her husband and proffered her hand. "Give me a hand up into the trap, but do remember my state!"

Soon they were all ready to go and, with a last wave to Meg and James, the Anderson family set off on their adventure into the unknown. The happy babbling of the children kept Christy's spirits up, but a kind of sadness fell upon her as they made their way out of the gate of Greenhouse and along the road past Hassendeanburn House.

Soon they were passing Lilliesleaf and the church there, where in the kirkyard lay her father and all his children from his first marriage. All were gone, but new members of the family had

Chapter 3

1822: A City

The arrival of the Anderson family in Greenock was something none of them would ever forget. At the end of their long journey from Greenhouse, they found themselves on the outskirts of Glasgow several days later. They were all tired and the younger children fractious but soon irritation changed to horror as they approached the city. Amid some very fine and impressively elegant buildings, the like of which they had never seen before, they also came across other unforgettable sights and smells.

They smelt the city before they arrived in its streets. Not only were they aware of the stink of the place, but also of the crowds of folk huddled in corners clutching bottles to their poorly clothed bodies, their filthy children meanwhile running around playing games in the squalor of the dung-strewn streets.

Christy noticed a drunken old hag in a greasy mutch who, with trembling hands, poured out some form of drink from her black bottle for a customer who paid and swigged it immediately before staggering off along the street. Later Christy was to learn that this drink was likely to have been a mixture of whisky and methylated spirits.

Soon their coach approached Greenock itself, a city referred to as 'Old Dirty', being deemed by some to be the dirtiest town in the west of Scotland. As they made their way through it to their new home, they could see why it had got its name. They passed more narrow and confused closes or alleys into which no sunlight could ever enter and in which ventilation was sadly lacking. Puddles of contaminated water plus human waste lay all around in these foul smelling and filthy alleyways, where more ragged children could be seen. Wretched mothers stood there with one hand clutching a babe attached to the breast, while the other held a bottle to her lips. All was dark and filthy and the stale stench of unwashed bodies pervaded the air.

George wondered why the people seemed to be living their lives in the streets instead of being inside their homes and was soon enlightened by the coachman who had recently been inside one of these dwellings visiting a man and his family.

"The poor soul bided in ain o' they closes with his wife and seven weans. Their stinkin' hame was one dingy room like a coal cellar wi' one small window and in the middle of this midden was one bed for all nine o' them. No wonder they go outside the close for some room an' air, though as you can smell for yourself it's no awfu' fresh."

The Andersons made their way through those appalling sights in silence, utter shock plainly sketched on every face. They were used to the tranquillity of the Borders countryside and, while George and Christy had come across some poverty in Hawick and Selkirk, it was nothing like this. Hassendean seemed like Illyria. That bewildering day made them realise they had left heaven behind and had now arrived in hell.

Then they came into sight of the mighty River Clyde. All eyes were again widened but this time in awe and wonder. They saw the extensive harbour with its many ships, the spacious quay with its massive sheds supported by iron pillars for the security of goods in transit. Beside it stood a mighty and impressive building of immense elegance facing the river with its large open space to the quay. This was the newly built customs house, which accommodated both the departments of customs and excise, and was where George would be working.

Here was Greenock, the sugar producing capital of Europe, with its sugar houses financed through the trade of captured African slaves. This triangular trade had ships leaving the Clyde to make their way to West Africa in order to exchange goods for captured Africans. These slaves were then transported across the Atlantic to the Americas to be sold as chattels to plantation owners in exchange for the sugar grown there. Ten years after the Andersons arrived in the west, Greenock's first Member of Parliament, appointed under the 1832 Reform Act, was Robert Wallace, a wealthy merchant who owned five plantations in Jamaica which had a combined total of 500 slaves. He was not alone, for at one time the Scots owned a third of the plantations in Jamaica, which was the largest producer of sugar in the Caribbean. Before the abolition of the slave trade, 400 ships were known to have plied their trade between the islands of the West Indies, across the Atlantic to Greenock and back again. When George learned of this trade, he remembered hearing of how his brother-in-law had returned from his first expedition on a slave ship and had recounted some truly distressing tales in his book, 'The Life and Travels of Mungo Park in Africa'.

But politics were not high on the family's list of priorities that day, for they were making their way to their new home at Port Glasgow, just outside Greenock. Very soon the coach took them to an altogether more pleasant area than that of the city with less smell and greater light. Rows of terraced houses faced the Clyde and were more openly spaced, some even having front gardens and it was in front of one of these that the coach finally stopped. 14 Patrick Street was to be their new home.

Port Glasgow had been the main port for the merchant ships from abroad, but as the river was deepened to allow ships to go straight to Glasgow and new road and rail links were made, the town was less and less needed as a port. The building of ships had become the main source of employment and industry. About ten years before the Andersons arrived, the town had celebrated the building of the 'Comet', the first commercial steam-powered passenger-carrying vessel in Europe, which sailed from Port Glasgow to the Broomielaw in Glasgow, greatly reducing the journey time.

Immediately after taking their cases down from the coach, George took a key out of his pocket and opened the black front door. Inside, the children rushed from the reception hall to explore the drawing room, the parlour and the kitchen with its decent-sized pantry. They quickly went up to the next floor and found five bedrooms – one for George and Christy, one for Margaret and Betsy, one for Christina and Janet, one for John and James, and the last was to be a spare room for visitors. The parents and children alike looked at each other and smiled. They were excited about their new home in spite of the wretched scenes they had witnessed on their way there, and it was not long before they began to unpack and make the house their home.

Then there was a knock at the door and, on opening it, they found that their new neighbour, the Rev. Nathaniel Morren, had come to welcome them. He himself had not long arrived from Aberdeen to take up his post as minister at the West Chapel in Blackhall Street, and a year later he was to bring his bride Mary to Greenock. The couples were to become good friends over the years and George in particular was to enjoy the pastor's quiet and grave humour, which harmonised admirably with the weight of his observations.

While Greenock may have been a total shock to the family initially, having left Greenhouse with its sense of space and order, the family were soon to enjoy the warmth and friendship expressed by their neighbours and others in Port Glasgow. Now they could claim to be city dwellers and each of them in their own way was ready to discover this new world.

In the September of that year, a baby girl was born to George and Christy. She was named Alice after her Aunt Alice Park. Three years later another child was born. This time it was a boy and he was called Thomas after his grandfather, Dr Thomas Anderson. Both babies were baptised in the Secession Church at Port Glasgow by the Rev. Dr David Inglis

And so, while George settled into his work and quickly made new friends, Christy got to know her neighbours while looking after her large family of three sons and five daughters. John and James attended the Grammar school, renowned for having educated James Watt of steam engine fame, and there they learned Greek, Latin, French, English literature, mathematics, trigonometry, drawing, geography, geometry and algebra. Meanwhile, Margaret, Betsy, Christina and Janet went to the new Highlanders Academy, a school originally built for the children of Highlanders but now attended by many from elsewhere. The two youngest ones, Alice and Thomas, were still at home.

Greenock and Port Glasgow, in spite of their initial impressions, proved to be a mixture of prosperous, hard-working, God-fearing residents and lawless, unemployed, unwashed poor. Some of the unemployed had come from the country but had not adapted to urban life, while others, drawn from many other places particularly Ireland, arrived looking for jobs but were lost in this foreign country. They were the unfortunates who found themselves living in dire squalor and certain poverty with pawn shops playing a large part in their lives.

In parlours and drawing rooms of the comfortably well off, many tales of the poor and their way of life were discussed. It was reported that some houses were without a stick of furniture, no bed, no table, no chairs but a chest for their few belongings and dirty wood shavings on the floor to rest the dwellers' weary heads. Often, following on to these observations, comments were made highlighting the fact that in spite of their poverty, these families appeared to produce countless unkempt, unfed and badly clothed children, which would be greeted by disapproving shakes of the head. Examples would be given of many poor little ones being allowed to wander the streets at any time of day or night. What was to be done? Did the parents not care about them? No, obviously not, was the usual answer. These parents were often too drunk to notice, and so school attendance was poor. Was it surprising therefore that these children turned to crime? Was it surprising that theft and housebreaking were common? Did the Church not teach that poverty, drunkenness and crime could all be attributed to the lack of religious faith in these people? It was usually agreed by those taking part in such discussions that these degenerates lacked a sense of morality. There was little sympathy or understanding for those who found themselves in such abject circumstances, for it was a belief held by many that the plight of the less fortunate was of their own making.

To the law-abiding citizens, such as the Andersons, the Sabbath was of utmost importance being ordained by God as a day for religious observance, for congregational worship, prayer and devotional reading. Christy knew that to neglect their religious duties was to dishonour God and risk divine wrath. How many times during her life had she heard stories of people who had broken the Sabbath by playing frivolous games or had been fishing or drinking and had been struck down by death or illness for the sin? Even cooking on the Sabbath was frowned upon and so on that day cold meats were served that had been cooked the night before. She, like all her friends and family, had been brought up expecting to stay indoors when they were not walking solemnly to and from church.

The Sabbath was a time for reflection and Christy recalled how she dreaded it when a child. She remembered the family services held at home in the evenings when first her grandfather at Hassendeanburn, and then later her own father at Greenhouse, would read a passage from the Scriptures. This would be followed by a prayer with all the family taking part and would finish with the communal singing of a psalm. And yet, despite all this misery she had suffered as a child, she now expected her children to suffer in the same way. She did, however, try to make the worship of the Lord a bit easier by telling them Bible stories at bedtime, while hoping they would at least gain a good understanding of the geography of the Holy Land. Sometimes she wondered if their understanding of that country was more familiar to them than that of their native land. They had all been baptised at home or in church, with the minister always officiating, most in the Borders, but Alice and Thomas in Port Glasgow.

Church played an important part in their lives, not just on the Sabbath but every day, and Christy, having been brought up to have a sense of a strict morality and to obey God's laws in this world, knew that to transgress would lead to an open confession of sin and sometimes a public penance as an example to others. The responsibility of discipline fell to the Kirk Session, members of which were expected to police the morals of the parish or congregation and when evidence was discovered of wrong-doing, such as extra-marital sex, drunkenness, brawling or profanity, the suspects were summoned to appear before the Kirk Session and tried as in a court of law. The most common sin was that of being an unmarried mother, and so over the years Christy had witnessed many a young girl sitting on the Black Stool, the Stool of Repentance. She, like all in her family, believed it to be right that, if a person were found guilty, he or she would be assigned a penance to be performed openly before the congregation as a public sign of contrition. Every Sunday morning, the Andersons would attend their neighbour's church in Blackhall Street with its austere and simple, white-washed walls and without any stained glass window, as plain glass was the norm in churches.

Like Christy, George had also been brought up in the ways of the established Church of Scotland but he was becoming influenced by the thinking of the Secessionist Church. He was also a regular reader of 'The Christian Herald' or 'Good Words', from which he got inspiration, from the accounts of social justice in the Old Testament and from the prophets or from the social teaching of Jesus.

Many an evening while sitting round the fire, the Rev. Nathaniel Morren and George, and sometimes the women too, would find themselves discussing the state of the church and society. As everyone knew, the economic downturn after the Napoleonic Wars had led to higher prices and unemployment, resulting in general unrest among workers. Attempts throughout the country had been made to achieve political reform and artisan workers had been particularly active in calling for strikes across Scotland. Bands of radicals had rallied, and many skirmishes had taken place with the armed forces that had been called out to deal with the threat of unrest, usually resulting in the arresting and even jailing of the ringleaders.

Two years before the Andersons arrived in Port Glasgow, five prisoners had been sent to Greenock to be imprisoned there because the prison in Paisley was full, and a mob had quickly gathered to protest. The five prisoners had duly arrived in a cart, escorted by the Port Glasgow Volunteers with a fife and drum playing, and put into the prison after which the Volunteers prepared to return to Port Glasgow. However, the crowd had turned on them with stones and bottles, hurting several of the Volunteers who fired a few shots in the air to warn the mob. This only provoked anger in the crowd and eventually the Volunteers had to fire in earnest, injuring and killing some of the mob, which then quickly gathered together their own weapons, eventually pulling up iron railings en route, and followed the Volunteers to Port Glasgow intending to fight. However, they dispersed quickly when they heard the militia were on their way via steamboat. Eight people were left dead, the youngest being a boy of eight and the oldest 65. Two years later, rebellion was still in the air throughout different parts of the country, which caused much discussion in the Anderson home.

By 1829, some of the Anderson children were joining in on the discussions and, while Alice and Thomas were a bit young to do so, Margaret now 20, Betsy 18, John 17 and James 15 took part. James in particular listened most intently and pondered on what he was hearing. Soon he had expressed an interest in going into the church and, of course, the Rev. Morren was delighted to hear this and spent many hours with the young lad in deep arrived. People, thought Christy, may change and so may some places, but the landscape of the Borders would no doubt live on forever. This thought reminded her of the words from one of Sir Walter Scott's poems, 'The Lay of the Last Minstrel'. She had learned the lines as they had appealed, and now they came back to her:

"Breathe there the man, with soul so dead
Who never to himself hath said
This is my own, my native land!"

discourse, while lending him many books on the subject. Christy was also pleased that her young son knew what he wanted to do as did her other son, John, who would most likely find himself in the nursery in Perth, working with her Uncle William and Archie, her brother. Her uncle was now an old man and had retired, and so she knew John's presence would be welcome.

But what of her five daughters? What was to become of them? Again, Christy found herself identifying with Mrs Bennett and not for the first time putting up a little prayer to God to encourage several single men 'in possession of a good fortune in want of good wives' to come along.

A year later, Meg, Christy's mother, at the age of 80, decided to come and visit them in Port Glasgow. However, on the way she was taken ill and died soon after. Her body was taken back to Lilliesleaf Churchyard, there to lie with her husband and the rest of the Turnbull family. At the service, the minister uttered the usual words of comfort and offered up a prayer and a reading at the graveside. Although the service had been private, the procession was public and so, on that cold autumn day, Christy found herself standing at the church door watching the bearers carrying the coffin, covered with the church's elaborately woven mort cloth, as it made its way to its final resting place. It seemed the end of an era with both of her parents gone. A little later, she was to find herself by the graveside with her two brothers, James from Greenhouse and Archie from Perth. Alongside them stood their old uncle, William Dickson, her mother's brother, who had made the long journey from Perth despite now being 78.

After the ceremony was over and everyone had dispersed, Christy took a little time by herself to visit the other Turnbull graves. Her mother had been buried beside her father and his first wife with all their children who had died before their time. Surely, Christy thought, she, James and Archie had been the lucky ones.

Chapter 4

1835: A Capital

Edinburgh. George stood beside Christy and their three eldest daughters, Margaret, Betsy and Christina, the girls having arrived in the capital for the first time. Not only were they in awe of the style and grandeur round about them, but they were also excited about visiting the fine shops. Margaret was to be married later that year to Dr John Leech and they were about to buy their dresses for the occasion.

While Christy was overjoyed that their first daughter was marrying a doctor, she prayed that it would be a marriage that would bring the young woman happiness. Margaret's intended husband was a serious young doctor from Ayr, dedicated to alleviating the poor in the Gorbals of the terrible diseases that were rife there. Only a couple of years ago, the country had suffered another bout of cholera and this young man was determined to seek out the cause. While she fully admired him for his dedication, she also wondered if he would have any time for his wife and family. But Margaret was now 25, and it was time for her to marry and make a new life for herself.

They had just completed their journey from Greenock, which George had been longing to do ever since the Union Canal had opened. They had begun their journey from Greenock on the Forth and Clyde Canal in a boat called a Swift which was pulled along by two horses. This took them through 11 locks from 110 feet above sea level down to the River Forth after which they crossed 85-foot aqueducts, each 900-feet long, which spanned the River Avon and on to Falkirk. There they were transferred to a flyboat for the next part of their journey. In it they went along the 31-mile Union Canal before reaching their final destination. On first hearing of the journey, the girls were unsure whether they wanted to travel this way, but George had persuaded them to do so and now there they stood at Port Hopetoun, feeling very proud of their achievements.

George was meanwhile trying to help secure a light stage-coach, which he eventually managed to do. The horses snorted a kind of greeting as he opened the carriage door to allow everyone to climb in, and their cases and boxes were lifted on board. Then, as they made their way down Lothian Road, Christy proceeded to give her family a guided tour. It had been many years since she had last visited Edinburgh, but she had prepared herself well for this visit by reading the 'Mercury' and learning all about the recent changes that had taken place. The architect, William Playfair, had wanted to achieve a visual unity of housing, squares and streets based on the images and styles of classical unity and now, as the New Town developed with its Grecian elegance, it was becoming known as 'The Athens of the North'.

Christy reminded her daughters that Edinburgh was the centre for Scotland's law and religion, and she could almost feel the city exude power and confidence not only from its buildings but also from its citizens. The new buildings being constructed, such as the Post Office, Registry House, the Royal Scottish Academy, the National Gallery and Art Gallery appeared to be fronted by Doric pillars and suchlike. Even the Theatre Royal at the end of Princes Street had been rebuilt.

Christy pointed out the incomplete monument standing high up on top of Calton Hill at the very end of Princes Street and explained that the intention was to build something akin to the Parthenon as a dedication to those who had fought in the Napoleonic Wars. However, it was not yet completed, as the Edinburgh Town Council had gone bankrupt a few years earlier. This piece of information she had acquired on her last visit to the capital from a Glaswegian lady, who had chuckled heartily at this state of affairs, reminding Christy of the age-old rivalry between the two cities.

Much as the girls politely showed some interest in their mother's guided tour, their real interest lay in Princes Street and George Street, as they were more than ready to explore the new shops there. They too had done their research and knew exactly where to go and what to buy. Nevertheless, not one of the three of them could ignore the grandeur of the mighty castle standing on its volcanic rock which, despite the new squares and gardens of the New Town and the historic alleys and churches of the Old, would forever dominate the city. Christy looked about her and smiled. She was glad to be back.

Their destination was to the south side of the city, to 40 Minto Street, where George's brother, Andrew, resided with his second wife and two small boys. He had recently retired from the army and from medicine. Now, he wanted to welcome his twin brother and his family who were to stay with them for a couple of days. During their stay, the plan was to also to visit their sister, Allie Park, now living in 5 Claremont Street.

It was a welcome change for Christy to be in Edinburgh, while knowing the younger family members, Janet 13, Alice 8 and Tom 5, were being safely looked after by the Morrens. John was already working in Perth with Christy's brother, Archie, while her other son, James, was in Edinburgh training to be a minister. George and Christy planned to visit him too, although they understood the life of a student was busy.

While travelling along Princes Street with its new Register House, Art Gallery, Post Office and Theatre Royal, the girls to their delight spotted Kennington and Jenner, the emporium which topped their list of shops to visit.

Before turning right on to the North Bridge, their driver explained why there was so much commotion outside the Waterloo Hotel.

"There's some big posh breakfast taking place over there now for the gentry because slavery's been abolished. Aye, tell that to some of us here in Edinburgh. Many of us are only one step away from that ourselves!"

Soon they were crossing the High Street with the castle ramparts towering over them at the top, while at the bottom sat the Palace of Holyrood, thus giving Christy an opportunity to share more of her knowledge. She reminded the family that these gloomy closes between these high tenements had witnessed so much over the years– the processions of Mary Queen of Scots going from palace to castle; John Knox railing from his pulpit in St Giles Cathedral; the countless burnings of witches at the stake or their drowning in the Nor' Loch, not to mention the hangings of many a notorious criminal at the Mercat Cross.

"And beside all this, just imagine the sight we missed of our present king, in all his tartan rigout, proudly parading up and down these streets when he visited the capital on the very day we moved to Port Glasgow nigh on fifteen years ago."

"I should have laughed at seeing him in the pink tights he wore because he thought his kilt was too short!" smiled George.

"I remembered wanting to be here at that time, but I was only a young girl" mused Margaret.

"And now you're a young lady and about to be a bride," smiled her mother gently. "That's much more exciting, I'm sure."

"Oh yes, Mama, but it would have been a dream to be married in Edinburgh rather than Greenock."

"You will be a dashing young bride with your handsome bridesmaids by your side, wherever the ceremony takes place. Greenock East will suit you just as well. And tomorrow you must make sure you choose the best outfits. The three of you will be every bit as fine as these ladies you see about you now."

Soon they alighted at the door of Andrew's home in Mayfield

and waiting for them was Andrew with Georgina and their two little boys. Christy was so pleased to see that life had turned out well for him eventually, after the tragedy of his young life.

"Welcome to Edinburgh. How marvellous to see you all. Let me help you with your things. It seems such a long time since we have been together."

Andrew, always a gentleman of some gravitas, gave a smile of genuine pleasure. Standing side by side, Christy could see the likeness between the twins, although her husband appeared larger and more robust. These two men had come from the same womb at the same time but had led such different lives.

"Come through to the parlour," said Georgina while gesturing to them to follow. "We have a surprise awaiting you."

And a pleasant surprise it was too, for in front of the fire stood a very attractive young lady, her smooth dark hair of ringlets and curls drawn into a large coil at the back of her head. She was dressed in a fashionable pink dress of a printed floral striped pattern and wore a light cashmere shawl around her shoulders. She was none other than Andrew's daughter, Anne, the little baby who had been sent home from Jamaica after her mother had died. She had been brought up by her grandmother, Mrs Cairns, and had just arrived from Peebles that very day. This little mite had blossomed into a delicate but beautiful 16-year-old, and her proud father took her hand while introducing her to her cousins.

"Now let me see if I can remember who is who, young ladies. You've all grown up so much since we last met, but I think I'm correct in naming you as Margaret, the-bride-to-be. Is that so?" He bowed to Margaret who nodded.

"And if so, you must then be Elizabeth because I have been told you look so much like your mother."

"Sometimes I'm called Betsy."

She also nodded while blushing, for she did indeed resemble Christy. She had the same fair hair, twinkling eyes and heart-shaped face, although the tiny waist that Christy had once possessed at Betsy's age had expanded over the years. Christy was also only too aware that the bloom of youth had long ago deserted her cheeks.

"Which means, of course, that you must be Christian?" Andrew said as he turned to the youngest in the group.

"Yes, Uncle, but Mama is called Christy as you know and so I am Christina, so people don't get us mixed up."

"Quite right, quite right, my dear. Now it is my turn to introduce my two sons. Come out of there, you scallywags."

Andrew turned to the door and brought forward two shy little boys.

"Come meet your cousins, you young lads. Show them your manners and bow like gentlemen."

Thomas and Andrew came forward and did as they were bid.

"And now, as your belongings have already been taken up to your rooms please settle down and take a dish of tea with us. You must be tired after your long journey."

And so the two Anderson families sat down together to get better acquainted, and to catch up on all the family gossip.

Sitting in the comfort of well-upholstered chairs by the warmth of the fire in the illumination of the mellow gaslight, the four older members of the company shared memories of times past, while the younger sisters sat together playing games or giggling and sharing information on the latest fashions to be seen. By this time, the little boys were asleep in their beds.

"How I used to envy you two long ago during the War, when I would picture both of you and Thomas and Margaret sitting by your own firesides in Scotland enjoying your peace and security. I did not believe I would ever experience the same. I always thought I was fated to spend my time in some unhealthy clime surrounded by death and destruction, while waiting for my own demise at the hands of either disease or 'Sma' Back' and his soldiers."

To Christy, the reference to Napoleon by his nickname brought back memories of Andrew's letters written so long ago. He had seen action in Sicily, been present at the sieges of

Flushing and Walcheren, as well as witnessing the terrible impact of yellow fever in Jamaica.

George smiled.

"At least you knew you had wages coming in regularly. Times were unsettling for us too, but I bow to your bravery and we're glad everything has worked out so well for you in the end."

"Aye, I well understand what you yourself have suffered what with the failure of your farm at Camieston. And I admire your bravery for venturing into the new world of Greenock. That must have been a great shock. Urban life can be ugly and cruel."

"Indeed it can be, but thankfully I managed to procure a job and now we've settled down and made good friends in 'The Dirty Town'. But we still miss the peace of the Borders and I know Christy yearns for the old ways of the countryside. Speaking of which, have you seen or heard much of brother Thomas, in Selkirk, recently? They say that dear Margaret is very ill and has not long to live."

Andrew nodded.

"We've heard just as much too. It will be a sad day when she leaves us, and Thomas and the bairns will miss her sorely. However, have you heard our nephew, Henry, has now qualified from the University here and is back in Selkirk sharing the practice with his father? He'll be a grand help to Thomas I'm sure. Did you know that Dr Knox was one of his anatomy lecturers at the 'varsity and where do you think they got their cadavers from for the anatomy lectures?"

"I have no idea," exclaimed George. His eyes then widened as he expected the answer. "Oh, no. Don't tell me they were supplied by these two scoundrels?"

"Which two scoundrels?" asked Margaret from the far corner of the room.

Her father turned to her.

"Burke and Hare, Margaret. They were the body snatchers from the High Street here who, when they realised there was money to be had for supplying bodies to the anatomy department, did not wait for death to take place naturally but helped their poor victims on their way. Many women of ill repute trying to sell her wares in the Canongate found themselves meeting their God before the appointed time."

"What happened?" enquired Betsy.

"Burke was hanged and Hare turned King's evidence. And we think that your cousin Henry might have been the recipient of some of these bodies to help him in his medical studies. Anyway, we hear Henry has now been awarded his degree and all's well that ends well."

"Except for Burke and Hare, father," replied Christina.

"Not to mention all the 'ladies of the night', the body snatchers' victims," added Margaret.

George took a sip of his 'dram' and nodded in agreement. Christy meanwhile supposed all these sinners would burn in Hell. It never occurred to her that night that perhaps these poor souls might have been young lassies from the country seeking honest work, but poverty had forced them to work on the streets. She could just imagine how perturbed the good people of the New Town must have been on learning of such horrors as they sat and talked in their fine homes or in the coffee houses. Although not really that far away in terms of distance, the Old Town and New Town of this city were worlds apart. Christy praised God that those she loved were sitting around her that night with food and drink enough, a roof over their heads and comfortable surroundings in which to live.

George quickly changed the subject. "Now, how is our 'lovely Allie'?"

His sister had often been addressed as such by her loving husband, Mungo, when he had been around. "Christy and I are planning to visit her tomorrow while the girls are making their way round the shops."

Andrew sighed, glanced at Georgina, and began to speak. "George, I wish I could tell you that our sister was well and content but I'm afraid I cannot do so. She is now all alone in that house of hers in Claremont Street, for young Archie is away in India and Elizabeth is now married and living in Wales. Life has not been kind to her."

With this, George and Christy nodded in agreement. How could anyone have forgotten what she had suffered? First her husband had disappeared in Africa, and then her first son, Mungo, had died in Madras in 1823 while working with the East India Company, only to be followed by the death of her youngest son, Thomas, when he went out to the Gambia to seek information on what had happened to his father.

"Allie lives surrounded by her memories."

"How old is she now, Andrew?"

"She must be over sixty but appears far older. The colour went from her cheeks a long time ago."

With that the clock on the mantelpiece struck midnight, and everyone was now ready to retire. It had been a long day but an exciting one. Christy had been especially pleased to be in the good company of Andrew and his family once more, and she knew how much it meant for both brothers to be together. Their paths had indeed gone in very different directions, but they were still twins and no matter how far apart in the world they had found themselves over the years, it was as if they had never been parted.

The next day dawned cold but bright and, while the girls got ready for a day of fun and frivolity seeking out the latest fashions in this enticing city, George and Christy made their way, slightly reluctantly, to 5 Claremont Street.

At mid-day they found themselves before the door of an elegant four-floored townhouse in one of the fashionable Georgian terraces of the New Town. After ringing the doorbell, they were ushered into the parlour by the maid where they found Allie sitting in the gloom of her surroundings. Unrecognisable and no longer the attractive, flirtatious and vivacious young woman of yesteryear, she was now a frail and thin old crone.

How time had changed things. Christy would never forget the

impact the young Allie had had on her on their first meeting so long ago, at her step-sister Esther's wedding to Mungo's brother, Alexander. Christy must only have been about 12 and Allie four years older. She remembered clearly how Allie had announced in no uncertain terms she was going to marry her father's apprentice, Mungo Park. Christy, of course, had learned later about how Mungo had helped Dr Anderson prepare his medicines before accompanying him on horseback to patients in all kinds of weather, at all times of day or night. The marriage had taken place three years later as Allie had foretold, and Christy could still picture the solemn young man adoring his light-hearted and playful young wife.

As Allie asked politely after the various members of the Anderson family, Christy recollected how proud the Park and Anderson families had been of the young explorer and how soon his fame had spread throughout Scotland and beyond. Mungo had been toasted in Edinburgh and London, and his book, describing his travels in Africa, had been read throughout the land. Even Georgina, the Duchess of Devonshire, had written a poem about him and the Niger. Very quickly, their children had come along and everything had appeared perfect. Certainly everyone knew Mungo to be a quiet and shy man, not at ease with many and preferring solitude to the busy family gatherings. However, it was not until later that his unseen episodes of pain and terror experienced in the night had become known and how Allie had comforted him so tenderly and so lovingly during his patches of acute anxieties. Although she had always been regarded as rather flippant and empty-headed, she nevertheless had always understood that Africa had been her rival for her husband's affections. Finally, having tried farming at Foulshiels and then having given thought to the family moving to New South Wales, Mungo had spent a few unhappy years practising medicine in Peebles, before deciding to return to the Gambia. Allie had understood her rival had won and let him go.

It had often been reported by his friend, Walter Scott, that, just before finally leaving Selkirk for good, Mungo had stayed the night with him at his home at Ashiestiel and the next day, as they were making their way back to Selkirk, Mungo's horse had nearly thrown him, its hoof having got stuck in a ditch. Throughout most of the previous evening Scott had tried to dissuade him from going back to Africa and when this incident had happened, he saw it as a bad omen. He expressed his concern but Mungo had dismissed the idea, gave Scott one final wave, and the friends had parted forever.

For years after Mungo's failure to return home, rumours had abounded as to what had happened to him. Allie and the family hoped and prayed to see him again but it was not to be and so she was left to bring up her family on her own.

Now, over a cup of tea, in this dimly-lit room surrounded by objects and pictures of happier times, Allie sat and listened to their news but didn't appear to be fully present. This sister of George's, who had once exuded energy and joy, seemed now to be only a weak and flickering flame calmly waiting to be extinguished. For her, life was over.

As George and Christy stood up to leave, she asked them to stay a few more minutes for she wanted to share something with them. Carefully she got up and crossed to the desk to where a piece of paper with some faded writing lay.

"I read this to myself every night and it comforts me when I cannot sleep. Let me read this to you now."

In her thin and faltering voice she read these words:

"Sleep on my sweet Babie, may nothing distress thee,
May sorrow like mine be a stranger to thee.
Thy father no more shall with rapture caress thee
No more will behold his sweet Babie and me.
Soft, soft be thy rest, thou companion of sorrow,
The morning of life it looks gloomy on thee,
Thy father is fallen in the Lowlands of Holland,
He sleeps far remote from his Babie and me.

Thy father is fallen, our stay and protector,
And with thee my Babie, ah! Where shall I flee?
The World, I fear, will sadly neglect us,
They feel not the wants of my Babie and me.
Dear image of him, who has left us forever,
Thou last beam of comfort allotted to me,
Through clouds of distress, shine forth on thy mother,
And cheer with a smile, her who lives only for thee."

George and Christy had heard Mungo's poem before, and knew it possibly referred to the death of an infant's father in the Lowlands of Holland during a campaign in 1799 when the British casualties had been heavy during a series of battles with Dutch and French troops. It may have been a lament for the widow and child of someone Mungo had known who had been killed then, but it could as easily have been written with regard to one of his own children.

Chapter 5

1840: A Dinner

Christy glanced out of the large bay window of Bellwood House and marvelled at what she saw. The house had been built on Kinnoull Hill and looked over the splendour of the plants and trees growing there, beyond which flowed the River Tay with the ancient city of Perth in the distance. In one direction stood the Grampians and, in the other, Moncrieff Hill. Bellwood commanded a view that could not easily be excelled.

So this was where James Dickson, her great uncle, had come in 1767 to open his nursery. He had seen the potential of the site, not only because of its advantageous light soil and southern exposure needed for good cultivation, but he must also have been aware that a bridge was soon to be constructed connecting the east side of the river to the west – also a great advantage. He rented the land on Kinnoull Hill, establishing the Perth Nurseries which expanded later to some 60 acres. However, he never stayed in the area, having business to attend to back home in the Borders and so William, his nephew and her uncle, ran the business for him.

Later, when James had died the business became William's. He then bought the land and in time he grew into a wealthy landowner, eventually earning himself the title Dickson of Barn-hill, having bought the lands of Barnhill and Knowehead. He also bought other property in the High Street, Blackfriars and Sprygate.

The last time Christy had visited Perth was to attend this uncle William's funeral in 1835, when she had been taken round part of the plantation by her brother, Archie, who had then become the owner of the business, having worked there since he was a young lad. Both William and Archie had been bachelors and Christy suspected Archie would remain so. His enthusiasm at that time had been tangible in the way he expressed his care for it all, from tiny seedlings to the largest of trees. He had shown her larches, spruce, Scots fir, pines, sycamores, beech and ash and had told her with pride about how they had imported trees from abroad, like the cedars from India and Lebanon, cypresses and redwoods from California, and others from Japan. While the sides and summit of Kinnoull Hill were now clothed in timber, lower down the Hill grew ornamental shrubs, rhododendrons, roses and orchids. Everything grown in the nurseries had to be able to withstand the severe winters with the full cutting blasts of the cold Scottish climate, whether the trees and plants were home grown or imported.

Not only had William left Archie the Perth Nurseries, now called the Dickson and Turnbull Nurseries, where 70 to 80 people were employed but also another nursery at Bridgend. Christy too had become a beneficiary of their uncle's will and the money left to her had helped her family live more comfortably in Greenock, as well as paying for her various daughters' weddings. Already Margaret, the eldest, had married Dr John Leech and was a mother to five-year-old Christina, while Janet, now more often referred to as Jessie, had married Dr William Turner, a surgeon in the Royal Navy, only the month before. Now in the following April, Christina was to be wed to Lewis Bilton, a captain also in the Royal Navy. How pleasant it had been to afford all the clothes and fripperies which came with such occasions.

Just before he had died, Uncle William had taken possession of the fine Baronial-style Bellwood House with its crow-stepped triangular gable ends and small turrets. It was now Archie's home, and now he was in the process of renovating it. He had invited her to Perth to inspect the house while, at the same time, visit her young son, John, now working there too. John was therefore the fourth generation to do so. However, the main purpose of this particular visit was to attend a dinner in Perth the following evening to be held in Archie's honour.

Christy turned away from the window and stepped back into the parlour. Her brother and John would soon be joining her for afternoon tea. Already the delicate china and tea knives were set out on the mahogany breakfast table in the centre of the room, together with the elegant silver monogrammed tea service taking pride of place. This had been fashioned for her Uncle William several decades before by the famous Edinburgh silver-smith James McKay. By the side of the fireplace stood a smaller tea table in which she had already discovered three hinged and tin-lined compartments containing green tea, black tea and sugar. Presumably Mrs Graham, the housekeeper, kept the keys to these drawers as tea was so expensive. Christy had heard tell that many a lady would carefully guard such a precious commodity, in case one of the servants was tempted to sample some.

Slowly, Christy moved around the room, admiring first the elegant desk. Her eye then went to the barrel organ and she wondered how it worked. She must ask for a demonstration. In the corner of the room, she discovered a little ornately carved mahogany table, which became a card table on opening it. Everything in the room was in order and in excellent taste, from the rug on the floor to the ruched curtains at the window; from the china to the silver; from the porcelain to the crystal. Everyone knew the parlour was the heart of the home and normally presided over by the mistress of the house but Archie, without a woman's touch, had still managed to make Bellwood a beautiful and comfortable home. Of course, Mrs Graham may have given more than some help in the choices made, for the house-keeper certainly kept the house in excellent order, making sure the servants were schooled in the black-leading and polishing of the fireplace, the burnishing of the steel fender and fire irons, not to mention all the daily polishing and dusting generally required.

All this was certainly a far cry from the farmhouse of Green-house overlooking the kailyard where Archie and she had been brought up. Of course, that had been a long time ago, but she could still cast her mind back to the days when they were young, running across the fields and guddling for trout in the nearby river. Little had she contemplated that she would end up in a city like Greenock with eight children, while Archie would become one of Perth's pillars of society.

That evening Christy, accompanied by Archie and John, made her way by coach and pair to the County Hall in Tay Street and arrived just as a group of musicians softly began playing medleys in the background. Christy marvelled at all the ladies and gentlemen of the Royal Horticultural Society of Perthshire who had come to pay their respects to Archie. She was particularly struck by the ladies' dresses with their very wide skirts puffed out by many petticoats, and she carefully noted the fashions for she had been instructed to do so by her daughters in order to keep them abreast of the latest styles. She must remember to tell them of the tightly-fitting bodiced dresses with their long fitted sleeves puffed at the top and their 'off the shoulder' décolleté necklines. Nor must she forget to add that the ladies, both young and old, wore long white silk mittens of net or open work, while on their heads bands of feathers were worn. She knew her daugh-ters would expect a detailed report on what she saw, but would she remember the details? And of course, they would want to know the materials worn and the colours chosen. Looking about her, she came to the conclusion that a mixture of muslin, satin, silk and organdie of many different hues, particularly yellow and white, was to be seen.

Soon it was time for the assembled company to take their

places at the tables set out across the large room, and with some ceremony John, her son, guided her to a table where he would be sitting by her side. Archie, of course, was at the top table. She marvelled at how the beeswax candles on the table made the crystal and silver twinkle, thus adding a magic sparkle to the scene.

The meal was then served to the 150 folk gathered there that evening. Christy had never in the past had to choose from such excellent fare. Cullen skink soup or cock-a-leekie was ladled out of large tureens, while already laid on the table were boiled gigots of mutton, roast haunches of venison, minced beef collops, assiettes of fowl and rabbit smothered with onions served with vegetable dishes containing cabbage, spinach, neaps, tatties and curly kale. After this came a choice of desserts such as Tay berries and burnt cream, cranachan or syllabub made with port wine. In case anyone was still hungry, apples, pears, nuts and dates were left on the table for guests to nibble during the speeches which were to follow. Throughout the evening, glasses were replenished with ale, Madeira, sherry, claret, Rhine wine and champagne but Christy however decided to stick to only one glass of wine.

When the dinner was eventually over and everyone felt replete – and some very merry – the Chairman, Sir Patrick Murray of Threipland and Fingask, stood up and invited the assembled host to toast first the Queen, then the Prince Consort, the Queen Dowager and the rest of the royal family. More toasts followed to the army and navy until finally, Sir Patrick requested the company to fill 'a flowing bumper' to toast the health of their esteemed guest, Mr Archibald Turnbull of Bellwood. There was a loud cheering from the assembled guests before the Chairman continued by mentioning the respect and gratitude that all members had for Mr Turnbull, especially as the honoured guest had managed to make the society more solvent, as well as helping the county of Perthshire to possess gardens and fruits equalled by few districts in Scotland and bettered by none. This speech was punctuated every now and again with loud cheers. The speaker then went on to describe Mr Turnbull's uncommonly active business habits, elegant taste and knowledge, both practical and scientific, of floriculture and horticulture as well as being ever ready and anxious to communicate to others the results of his experience.

Christy was proud to hear reference to Archie's kindly and generous nature and was most impressed when Sir Patrick illustrated this with a quotation from one Perth worthy who had said "It's weel for me to speak weel o' the gentleman, for he's aye ready to help us, and if we need ony favour, he's aye the first to offr't." Christy could not agree more with this sentiment, for her brother had always shown the greatest interest and kindness to his family, especially his nephews and nieces. He had encouraged them in their interest in horticulture, just as three generations before him their great-grandfather Robert Dickson at Hassendeanburn had done with his family. Now here was her son, John, continuing the tradition.

The speaker then finished with warm wishes for Archie's long and continuing valuable services, and this was followed by a toast protracted by cheering.

How proud Christy felt. How proud their parents would have been to have seen their son honoured in such a way, but alas both were now dead. However, she knew their other brother, James, still living at Greenhouse, would be delighted to read the report of the evening in the next day's Perth Advertiser, which she must remember to cut out and send.

It was then Archie's turn to speak. He stood up and spoke well but briefly, expressing his heart-felt thanks for the very high and flattering honour given him, but he was aware that the company was now ready to move on and enjoy the rest of the evening talking to friends and dancing reels and strathspeys which was to be played by the excellent band.

Christy had been promised there would be songs later using the lyrics taken from Sir Walter Scott's 'The Minstrelsy of the Scottish Borders' and set to music by the composer Franz

Schubert, for these songs had been deemed appropriate for the 'honoured guest', Archie having been brought up near Hawick. Whether these songs were ever performed or not, Christy was not able to vouch, for there was so much talking and laughing and chinking of glasses around her it was difficult to hear.

On returning home eventually and after wishing everyone goodnight, Christy made her way to her bedchamber while experiencing a warm glow from the small amount of wine she had drunk and the excitement of being involved in such an evening. Certainly she was now tired, but she did not forget to kneel by the bed and pray as she always had done, thanking God for the goodness bestowed on her and her family.

While praying, she opened her eyes and caught sight of herself in the mirror. She was certainly no longer that young girl who, all these years ago, had excitedly described her stepsister's wedding to her grandmother, for she was now a grandmother herself and for a moment she reflected on her life. It had not always been easy and most of the years seemed to have been taken up with financial worries, but she had always known she had married the right man and for that she had no regrets. Her abiding concern had always been for her five daughters and the hope that they would make successful marriages. But now, she could begin to relax for only Betsy and Alice were still to find husbands. As for her sons, James was now a qualified minister of the Church of Scotland, John had settled happily here in Perth, and Thomas was still a schoolboy. She closed her eyes and put up a prayer to God to protect these children and the grandchildren who would no doubt follow. The world was rapidly changing, and she prayed for these offspring to be safe and happy.

Part 4

Elizabeth's Story

Chapter 1

1848: A Chat

The tearoom of Kennington and Jenner was bustling with energy, refinement and gentility on that warm summer's afternoon. The large windows looked out across to the castle and the view reminded Betsy of that day, so long ago, when her family had come across to the capital to choose outfits for Margaret's wedding. Now, here she was back again more than 14 years later.

What a pity their mother had not been alive to know that her five daughters had in the end managed to find suitable husbands. How relieved she would have been, as this had been her lifelong worry. She had at least witnessed three weddings. Having attended Margaret's wedding to Dr John Leech in 1835, she had also witnessed that of 18- year- old Jessie's to 53- year-old Dr William Leech in 1840. He had been a naval surgeon and had served at Waterloo but had sadly died only three years after the marriage. She had also attended Christina's to Captain Lewis Bilton. However, she never lived to be present at either Betsy's own wedding in 1849, or that of Alice, who had just been married the previous day in Edinburgh to James Miller, a solicitor in Perth.

Now Betsy was sitting waiting to meet her older sister, Margaret, to share afternoon tea and a chat. However, she was early and so she began reflecting on how her own marriage had come about and how she had first met her husband, Andrew, in 1841. She had been working as housekeeper to her Uncle James at Greenhouse at the time, for he was by then a widow with a young son but then he had decided to sell up and buy another farm at Peel, not far away. Her father had come from Greenock to help with the removal, for it was the least he could do for this brother-in-law who had given him a job and had taken him and the whole Anderson family in when her father had lost the tenancy of his farm.

While they were busy at Greenhouse, she remembered her mother being in Selkirk helping George's brother, Thomas, care for the dying Isabella, her sister-in-law. Isabella had never married and had lived her life at the Dovecote with her brother and family. Sadly, Betsy's mother, Christy, herself had died three years later.

But Betsy smiled as she remembered how her older sister Margaret, at that time had been left in Greenock during their parents' absences to be in charge of their sister, Alice, brother, Thomas, plus Margaret's own daughter, Christina, and their young cousin, James, who had been sent from Greenhouse while the removals were taking place. Margaret had found her young charges somewhat of a handful, no matter how hard she had tried to be a disciplinarian.

Back at Greenhouse, during that time, Betsy had gone with her uncle and father to Lilliesleaf Church one Sunday morning and, after the service, had accompanied her uncle to visit the grave-yard where his late wife was buried. While there he happened to introduce her to a neighbour, a Mrs Dodds from Hillhead Farm, and her son, Andrew, a theology student in Edinburgh, who was that day making one of his regular visits back home to see his family. Betsy remembered him as being very intense and very serious, but nevertheless very likeable. Something about him reminded her of the Rev. Nathaniel Morren, their neighbour back in Greenock.

But it wasn't until three years later, after she had looked after both of her ailing parents in Greenock until they had died, that she and Andrew were to meet again. She had just returned to the Borders to continue her work as housekeeper to Uncle James, now living in Peel, and one morning had decided to go to the Lilliesleaf graveyard with some lilies to place on her parents' memorial stone, her father having died not long before. When she got there, she knelt down to read the inscription:

"In memory of George Anderson born in Selkirk in July 1784 and who died at Greenock. Also of Christian Turnbull born at Greenhouse in 1784 and died at Greenock in the sixty years of her age. They will sleep on."

As she was doing so, she had become aware of a presence beside her and, on standing up and turning round, she found herself once more face to face with this Andrew Dodds. Again, he had been back visiting his mother and was visiting his father's grave, but by that time he had become an ordained minister of the United Presbyterian Church in Avonbridge in Stirlingshire. Very soon they were often in each other's company both in the Borders and Edinburgh but never of course alone. Sitting there in Kennington and Jenner that day, she reminisced about how, on various social occasions, she had patiently stood by his side and listened to him talk with other men on the present state of religious affairs in Scotland.

One subject which was of particular interest to them all was the Disruption of the Church of Scotland which had taken place only three years before when, at the General Assembly in Edinburgh, two thirds of the ministers had walked out in protest against the patronage of the Established Church. These brave men, by doing so, gave up their manses and their livings to set out in faith in order to establish the Free Church, believing it was wrong that landowners had the right as heritors to have the power to appoint parish ministers. This had all happened in St

George's Church in George Street, the road just behind the one in which she was seated.

One evening, when Andrew had asked her if she would be prepared to be his helpmate and to take up the challenge of becoming his wife, she accepted his proposal and in the following year they were married in Muiravonside Church.

But here she was now in Edinburgh, surrounded by the ladies and gentlemen of Edinburgh society enjoying the delights of the tearoom and each other's company. Betsy watched the scene for a little while, but soon began to muse on what had happened to her sisters. Margaret had for some reason not stayed in the Gorbals with her husband for long. She took Christina her daughter with her and spent the following years visiting various relatives, particularly those in Perth where her brother, John, and sister, Jessie, were living. Jessie had no children but instead of a mother had become housekeeper to their Uncle Archie at Bellwood. Betsy's other sister, Christina, with her two-year-old son Lewis, also spent much time at Bellwood, her husband being away at sea much of the time. Now, Alice too would be living in Perth – but not at Bellwood – with her solicitor husband. As for her brothers, John was of course in Perth working with his uncle but living in his own house, while Thomas, the youngest, was a doctor practising in Perthshire. It seemed therefore that for most of the Anderson family, Perth had become home. She and her other brother, James, now a minister living in Norham in Berwickshire, were the only two not to find their futures in the 'Fair City'.

"Betsy!"

She heard her name called across the clatter of cups and voices, as Margaret came towards her. Betsy thought her sister looked somewhat down at heel compared with those around them and appeared older than her 39 years. But then, on reflection, her life had not been easy and certainly not the one envisaged. Betsy then realised that Margaret was no doubt thinking the same of herself, as she was dressed in the dowdy dark attire of a minister's wife which discreetly covered any evidence of her pregnancy.

However, as soon as she had greeted her sister, ordered afternoon tea, and settled down for a chat, Betsy told her sister the good news.

"I am aware I surprised you all by getting married, as everyone had regarded me as the spinster sister for whom it was too late to marry, but as you know I managed to do so and now, at the grand old age of 36, here I am expecting a baby."

"A baby! How wonderful, Betsy! When is it due?"

"October."

"Well done. Mama would have been so proud of you," added Margaret.

Betsy ignored the slight condescension of the remark, finding it vaguely ironic considering her sister's own circumstances. Margaret had married Dr John Leech over a decade ago and had set up home in the Gorbals of Glasgow where he worked and where Christina, their daughter, had been born, but for some reason she had not stayed long there. Perhaps she had wanted to escape from the grinding poverty of the place with its insanitary, overcrowded conditions and no proper drainage; perhaps John had dedicated himself too much to solving the problems of killer diseases such as small pox, typhoid, consumption and cholera, and to fighting for the supply of soft water to the area.

He had certainly achieved much for eventually, thanks to such persuasive people in the medical fraternity like himself and others, the Reform Act had been introduced and councils were forced to take money from the local rates in order to pay for the cleaning of the streets. Among other things, the Act made sure that slaughterhouses followed strict rules; a precaution that had an impact on the quality of food and diet. John's dedication had paid off and during the next cholera bout to hit Glasgow, his area had only been mildly affected, thus providing the evidence he had been seeking that there was a link between water, dirt and disease.

Yes, he had been successful, but perhaps at the expense of his family? Margaret never spoke about what happened and Betsy could only guess. Now Margaret was living at Bellwood but on that day was staying in Edinburgh at their cousin Clara's house in Rutland Street.

"Did you have time to speak to Jessie yesterday?" Margaret continued. "Everything has worked out so well for her and Uncle Archie. It seems that she is not just acting as his housekeeper but is involved in the running of the business too."

The thought of the splendour of the house in Kinnoull reminded Betsy of her own very different circumstances in Slamannan, a place of misery, ugliness and poverty, although not in her own home. To her, Kinnoull was another world, peopled by gentile society and refinement.

However, Betsy was not about to discuss Slamannan with her sister. Instead, the two of them went on to discuss Alice's wedding which had taken place the day before and the family members who had attended. Their four uncles had been there, James and Archie Turnbull their mother's brothers, and Thomas and Andrew Anderson, their father's brothers.

"They are all quite remarkable and it was splendid to see them all there yesterday," remarked Margaret.

Betsy could not agree more. Uncle James was still farming at Peel; Uncle Archie was running his nursery business in Perth; Uncle Thomas was administering to the sick people of Selkirk; and Uncle Andrew was doing the same in Edinburgh. They were now all in their sixties, except Archie who would join the sexagenarians the following year.

"And they all look so well, although Clara is not happy about her father's health.

Uncle Thomas has worked so hard all these years, riding about in and around Selkirk on horseback in all weathers. It cannot have been good for him."

Betsy agreed. "Just like his father before him."

They paused again for a moment, each picturing their grandfather, the first Dr Thomas Anderson. Perhaps their long dead relative, Mungo Park, was right in giving up the job of surgeon in Peebles. Not that his suspected demise had anything to recommend it.

Margaret broke the silence.

"I wonder if Henry Scott will carry on in the same manner."

They both shrugged. They both liked their cousin who was now running the Anderson family practice in Selkirk along with his father, Uncle Thomas. With a little giggle, Margaret added, "I love listening to his stories of his medical student days under Dr Knox. How he loves shocking us all with those tales of working on the cadavers brought in by Burke and Hare. How he revels in that."

"Talking of Henry Scott," Betsy interjected, "he must be delighted in having Alexander home from China, although it will be quite a shock for Alexander and his family to come from Hong Kong to Jedburgh."

She was referring to their other cousin, Dr Alexander Anderson, the brother of both Henry Scott and Clara, who had gone out to China over 10 years before as personal medical attendant to Lord Napier, first living in Macao and then in Hong Kong as Assistant Surgeon to the British Consulate. Now he had decided to return home and did so with his wife and family, to take up a practice in Jedburgh.

Margaret looked puzzled and then said, "He must be about our age, but I can barely remember him. I did take to his wife, Eliza. I don't think there's been a New Yorker in the family before. They must have some interesting stories to tell about their time in China."

Betsy nodded. "Yes. They were involved somehow in the opium wars, or so I'm led to believe. I must make a point of visiting them in Jedburgh and finding out more. Did you know they've moved into Abbey Green House there? Oh, and speaking of the Borders, I was thinking of Anne Bathgate the other day."

Anne, Uncle Andrew's daughter by his first marriage who had been born in Jamaica and who they had met on their sojourn to Edinburgh before Margaret's wedding, was now married to John Bathgate, a Peebles lawyer, and had a family of her own.

Margaret sighed. "You have obviously not heard the latest news. She is dying of an ovarian tumour and she's not even 30. John will be left with four young children to look after."

Betsy put down her cup and almost choked. "I didn't know. That is horrible. Life can be so cruel to some. Poor Anne, and after experiencing such a cruel entry into the world."

After sharing such sad news, Margaret brought up the subject of a happier event.

"Where is your baby going to be born, Betsy? Are there any decent hospitals around where you live?"

"I've been advised to have the child in Edinburgh because of my age. Otherwise, I should be quite happy to give birth at home. I don't suppose you know anything about the maternity provision here."

"As it so happens, my dear, I was speaking to Clara on that very subject. Why don't you write to her? Alexander can offer guidance."

Clara, their cousin and daughter of their Uncle Thomas in Selkirk, was now married to Dr Alexander Peddie, and living in Rutland Street where Margaret was staying that day.

"Did you know he is a great supporter of Dr Simpson, the one involved in the use of chloroform? According to Clara, Alexander is also a strong advocate of its use in controlling pain in childbirth. Of course, your Andrew may not be in favour of the method, for didn't I read somewhere that the Church is against such a practice? Now where did I see that?"

Margaret picked up 'The Scotsman' newspaper which she had put down on arriving at the table and quickly found the very article on the subject.

"Yes, here we are." She squinted at the paper.

"It says that the Church is taking their teaching from the book of Genesis in which it states: 'To the woman he said,' – God

I presume – 'I will greatly increase your pains in childbearing; with pain you will give birth to children. Your desire will be for your husband, and he will rule over you.' So, the Church seems to believe we must suffer. What is Andrew's view on the subject? Have you asked him?"

Betsy shook her head. "But if that is the view of the Church, then no doubt I won't be using chloroform, but I shall have to discuss it with Andrew and he will advise me."

"Well, it's worth considering. It states here that 60 births have already taken place here in Edinburgh in the last year with the use of chloroform. According to Alexander, Dr Simpson dislikes the use of ether because of its smell and the amount needed. He also points out there is a danger of explosion if ether is used near a live flame and, as much of surgery is done by candlelight, it is a risk."

"You seem to know a great deal about it, Margaret. You're not contemplating another child, are you?"

"As I rarely see John, I think there is little chance of that. One child is enough. No. Dear Clara gave me this article to read this very morning. She is obviously interested in it for herself in that she gave birth in May and no doubt is contemplating having more children. I shall leave the newspaper with you and you can take it home for Andrew to read."

Suddenly Margaret noticed the time on the clock on the wall nearby and stood up.

"I must hurry now and call in at Christina's school. She's attending the Merchant Maiden Hospital and I promised I would meet her there when school was finished. She's a boarder and loves it. But what a price for all the clothes! The girls all seem to wear sumptuous dresses of silk with buttons from neck to hemline. You can imagine how long that takes to sew on, but they do learn dressmaking and needlecraft which helps. Christina seems to spend all her time sewing."

Betsy stood up to bid farewell to her sister, who not only gave her the newspaper but also a book she had brought.

"Oh, and before I forget, here's a book to be getting on with.

Clara also gave it me. It's by someone called Currer Bell. He's written a remarkable story there. I'm sure you'll enjoy it."

The sisters kissed each other on the cheek and soon Margaret was on her way. Betsy then sat down and relaxed. It was good to sit still for a moment. The world always seemed to be rushing. The pace of life had changed so much so quickly.

She wondered how things really were in the Leech family. Certainly, Margaret had always expressed her admiration for her heroic husband but perhaps, when faced with the reality of day-to-day living in the slums around her, her optimism had waned and she had decided not to bring Christina up in such disease-ridden circumstances. Betsy had not seen this brother-in-law for years; for he had attended none of the weddings including the one the day before, but then neither had her own husband for Andrew could not spare the time.

She sat back in her chair and looked about. Amid the chatter and laughter, the clinking of cups and the laying of plates, she watched the cream of Edinburgh society mingle. She noticed the fashionably dressed ladies in their poke bonnets and wide dresses, their cashmere shawls and small folding carriage parasols by their side. So this was Edinburgh society. These were the people who lived in the New Town with its squares and crescents, its parks and gardens, its theatres and art galleries, its churches and assembly rooms, its shops and tearooms. A far cry from Avonbridge.

However, it was a city of two halves, and while one half was a place of great wealth and economic dynamism, the other still housed crumbling tenements of disease, filth, poverty and crime. Andrew was always reminding her of the grossly unequal distribution of wealth in Scotland, no more apparent than in this city where, he declared, the stench of the Old Town, more than any numbers of learned treatises on mortality, was a stark reminder of the scale of the sanitary crisis.

She then glanced down at her swelling body and wondered what life would be like for this unborn child. Would it be a girl or a boy? If a boy it was sure to be called Andrew, after Andrew's father; if a girl, Christian, after Betsy's own mother as was the custom. Betsy sighed. Yet another Christian in the family. Would the child stay in Avonbridge or venture further afield? What would life be like in the future in this ever-changing world? So much was happening, so soon, so fast. What would the rest of this century bring forth?

She suddenly become aware of the time and so paid the waitress, stood up and picked up her bag lying on the table. Then she collected the newspaper left by Margaret together with the book. She glanced down at its title. 'Jane Eyre'.

Chapter 2

1856: A Plan

Betsy carefully folded her shawl over the tiny body of the dead child and handed it to the 'howdie', who she knew would dispose of the body, the midwife having done it so many times before with other babies. Then she turned and looked at the ailing mother, already suffering from consumption and not, it seemed, having many days to live herself. How unlucky some were, Betsy thought, to be born into such conditions.

She looked at the recessed bed in its cracked damp wall where the poor, young mother was lying, and then down at the brick and loosely-laid wooden floors, followed by a glance up to the dirty and low, broken cracked ceiling with its red roof. She shuddered in spite of the heat coming from the fire in the small cooking range, knowing full well that the coal needed to keep it going was stored underneath the bed. The little light there was came through the small panel windows, one in the front of the slum cottage and the other to the back of the building, plus from the paraffin oil lamp sitting on the table nearby.

The stench of dirt was so stifling she could hardly breathe, for in this slum dwelling like most others there were no places to put refuse and no toilet facilities of any kind. Drainage for such a home was only an irregular cutting in front of the house, which had long ago become a cesspit. For water, the family would be depending on rainwater from the roof caught in the barrel outside, or from the muddy stream. Whatever water the inhabitants received for their drinking, cooking and washing was unfiltered and far from pure. It was little wonder that such deaths as that of this little baby and soon that of his mother were so commonplace in Slamannan.

All this was a far cry from the conditions in which Betsy had found herself eight years before, when she had given birth to her own daughter – without chloroform – in a comfortable bed in her cousin Clara Peddie's Edinburgh house in Rutland Street. On that day, there had been a highly skilled midwife to help deliver her baby and plenty of clean water on hand. Andrew had wanted the best for his wife and child and was not prepared to trust the local 'howdies' in Slamannan. Later, he had christened the baby at his church in Avonbridge under the name of Christian Turnbull Dodds, known soon after as Chrissie. She was called after her grandmother Christian Turnbull, known as Christy, who in turn was named after *her* grandmother Christian Thomson, known as Chris.

Avonbridge had originally been a small farming community with only a few houses in the village, but now it was changing fast. It lay on both sides of the River Avon with the largest part being in the parish of Slamannan and the lesser in the Muiravonside parish, a medieval parish of picturesque and undulating hills. The old one-arched stone bridge spanning the river was part of the parish road leading from Falkirk to Bathgate.

The villages of Avonbridge and Slamannan were known, along with two others, as the Southern Braes villages. They were on the windswept Slamannan plateau where the soil was prone to flooding from the River Avon, causing much of the upper areas to be damp and infertile moorland. Farming had always been a problem. The name Slamannan, it was said, was derived from a corruption of what an early farmer was believed to have said to

141

his feudal landlord: 'ploughing this land would slay man and mask.' Still, it supported 39 farms, but the harshness of the conditions on the plateau meant that crops were harvested months later than those in the lower and more fertile fields. A further problem for the inhabitants of the Southern Braes villages was their relative isolation, exacerbated by a lack of transport links. Life there was particularly harsh during the winter months. However, despite this, the people there had worked on the land for generations as well as being millers, joiners, masons, shoemakers, weavers, tailors and the like.

Then in 1822, the 30-mile Union Canal had been built connecting Edinburgh to Falkirk, with its three huge aqueducts over the River Almond, the Water of Leith and the River Avon. Betsy well remembered the remarkable journey the family had taken by way of the Canal on their visit to Edinburgh to prepare for Margaret's wedding and how it had carried them across the steep-sided River Avon valley, 85 feet above the river level.

In 1840 everything changed again, for the twelve and a half mile Slamannan Railway was built and in doing so, the cutting of the land had revealed fine seams of coal and other minerals. Soon therefore bores were being made in the land, to be followed by the opening up of pits all over the parish. The Industrial Age had arrived and these new industries needed coal, iron and slate. Stone was also in demand and so, as well as the opening up of coalmines, stone quarries began to appear in order to produce the sandstone and granite needed for the houses of the New Town of Edinburgh. Previously goods had always been trans-ported by the Union Canal to Glasgow and Edinburgh, but now the Slamannan Railway was carrying coal, iron, granite, slate, stone, sandstone and cobbles to their destinations.

Of course all this development had needed workers and so newcomers had begun to arrive. What had once been a quiet rural collection of a few houses began to grow into a larger village. However, as the workers in these mines and quarries were very poorly paid, they and their families found themselves living in slums and it was in one such dwelling that Betsy found herself standing.

Often, over the years, Betsy had found the life of a minister's wife in such a place, with parishioners living in such conditions, hard to take. Although she had seen similar living conditions in Greenock where she grew up, she and her family had lived in reasonably comfortable surroundings and, while they had certainly witnessed great misery in some parts, they themselves had had little to do with it. Now, however, as a minister's wife, her role was to visit the families of the parish in their bleak, damp and filthy hovels.

The original good people of the parish had been quiet, well-behaved and mindful of the teachings of the Bible and had utter respect for the Sabbath, but these incomers had different ways of living, often having little or no belief in God. However, Andrew believed that it was the Church's duty to look after the weak and the sick and not to blame the poor, the vagrants, the drunks and the prostitutes for their own downfall. Hard work, self-help, thrift and temperance were the answer and social improvement came with moral improvement. His intention was therefore to bring his flock to the Church, in order to save their souls.

After gathering up her basket and putting on her bonnet, Betsy bade farewell as best she could to the miserable scene and made her way back home. As she went, she reflected on the many tragedies of childbirth she had witnessed over the years because of the poverty and insanitary conditions on the plain. But she was also aware that tragedies could happen even when conditions were good. Had Alice, her youngest sister, on giving birth only the previous year to a little girl named Grace, not die a few months later as did the child? She had only been 31.

Naturally, all the family had been stunned by the turn of events. For Betsy it was a particular blow as she and Alice had been very close, having been the two sisters who cared for their parents in Greenock until they had died. Then Betsy had married

Andrew and then Alice had married James Miller. How could anyone forget that happy June day in Edinburgh when their brother, James, a minister of the Presbyterian Church in Norham, had performed the ceremony? Everything had seemed perfect and that nothing could go wrong. Then it did.

Sometimes, Betsy found it hard to believe that God was a loving god and that it was ordained in Heaven that He could take Alice from James and from their little children, all under the age of seven. But then she remembered He was also a vengeful God and she felt anger as well as grief.

She also felt angry that miners and their families here in Slamannan had to live in such shocking conditions, no matter how hard they worked. These people had little to celebrate and perhaps little reason to believe in the existence of the Almighty, especially when others, no more deserving, could ride about in their fine carriages, dressed in their fine clothes.

As she walked up the road past other slums, out of which poured suffering and misery at every door, she vowed she must get away from this grinding poverty if only for a few days. She had always appreciated how lucky she was to be able to contemplate this, when for many people in Slamannan there was no such chance of escape.

And she also knew where she wanted to go. She was craving to visit the bonny Borders again and see the members of the family who were still there. In Selkirk, Uncle Thomas of course had now passed away leaving his son, Henry Scott, her cousin, to continue as the local doctor there. He was the third generation in the family to take on the role in the town. Meanwhile his brother, Alexander, back from Hong Kong, had set up a practice in Jedburgh. It was to both these cousins and their families she wished to visit. Her old Uncle James at Peel had also died and had had left her £300 in his will, no doubt for her having been his housekeeper, plus a portion of a sum divided equally between his nephews and nieces. Somehow, Betsy felt that the legacy would never make up for the loss of the old man but it did give her the freedom to travel if she wished, although legally the sum belonged to her husband.

Betsy vowed to discuss her plan with Andrew that evening, knowing full well he would understand and allow her to go. She planned to put flowers on her uncle's headstone and on that of her parents in Lilliesleaf graveyard, before making her way to Selkirk to visit Henry Scott. Then she would move on to Jedburgh to see Alexander. She would take her little eight-year old Chrissie with her and show her the farm at Greenhouse where she had been born before living in Greenock. Perhaps she might even visit Hassendeanburn House where an elderly relation lived. How good it would be to bring some clean air into the child's lungs and let her smell the sweetness of the countryside.

Both Henry Scott and Alexander were around the same age as her, but they had all lived totally different lives. She had kept in touch with Henry Scott and saw him from time to time, but Alexander she knew less well as he had gone out to China a number of years ago as Assistant Surgeon attached to the mission of Lord Napier, the first British Superintendent of Trade in Qing China. Then, he had worked as Surgeon to the British mission, assisting the British ships with no surgeons on board, and later became Macau's Agent for the Seaman's Friend Association in Canton, its objective being to promote the welfare of seamen. Betsy had been told that some of the 17 founders of the Association had been European and American merchants (mostly opium traders and shippers), while the others were Protestant missionaries. Eventually he had moved to Hong Kong to be in charge of the dispensary there and had had sat on the Hospital Establishment Committee along with his fellow Scot, James Matheson, of the extremely successful opium firm Jardine and Matheson. Finally, before coming home, he had become the first Colonial Surgeon in Hong Kong. However, that appointment had been short-lived since the position was created without the authorisation of the British government and so, after much wrangling, he and his American wife, Eliza, came home with their family to Jedburgh to practise medicine once more. Rumour had it that his wife's brother, Charles, had also been in China, but had returned home to America bringing with him three Chinese servants, thought to be the first Chinese immigrants to set foot in the United States.

As she entered the front door, Betsy heard voices and recognised them as those of Andrew and the Rev. James Brown, a clergyman friend from his student days in Edinburgh. She sighed for she knew, as much as they liked and respected each other, they would spend many hours arguing over the complications of the Church of Scotland as it stood now.

Her predictions were correct for throughout lunch and during the afternoon, the two men discussed the Westminster Confession and how it should be regarded. Betsy had heard this discussion so many times before. The original belief of the Church was that human nature was totally depraved as a result of the original sin of Adam's disobeying God's command, and this had brought about the fall of all humankind. Betsy, like everyone else, had been brought up believing that we are all born in sin, selfishness and wickedness, and thus are all deserving of damnation, unless we repent before death. However, the Presbyterian Church and its clergy had moved on and supported the ethos of a warmer, activist faith, but one that still inspired a profound fear and insecurity.

While both men supported social progress and possessed a more humane, social attitude, they did not, however, seem to agree entirely about everything. Subjects such as the anti-slavery movement, the campaigns for child welfare and the efforts to reduce the number of hangings were three such issues, as was what should be taught in schools. Nor did they agree about the introduction of the organ in the church to help with the singing of hymns. In retrospect, it seemed to Betsy that they didn't agree on much. Anyway, she had heard all the arguments for and against these issues many times, and so eventually she only half listened to the conversation as it proceeded. Instead, while busily sewing her sampler, she planned her trip to the Borders and, once the guest had at last taken his leave, she mentioned the idea to Andrew. He of course did not refuse her suggestion and thought the whole idea an excellent one.

However, Betsy never did meet her cousin in Jedburgh, for a few days after her decision to visit the Borders, a letter arrived. Alexander had died.

Chapter 3

1861: An Education

Her daughter stood in front of the looking glass and, with a twirl of delight, admired what she saw. Meanwhile, Betsy looked on with pride. The twelve-year old Chrissie was already turning into a very attractive young lady and looked remarkably like Betsy herself at the same age with her small waist, feet and hands, the same twinkling eyes and infectious smile. Chrissie, however, had a greater confidence and poise than Betsy had ever possessed, and had a certain air of mischief and energy, ready to challenge any difficulty which might arise.

Betsy was visiting Chrissie that day at the Merchant Maiden Hospital in Archibald Place where the girl was a boarder. It was, of course, not a hospital but the only private boarding school for girls in Edinburgh, founded back in1694 by Mary Erskine. Margaret, Betsy's sister, had thoroughly recommended the establishment as her own daughter, Christina, had already attended the school some years earlier and had been very happy there.

While Chrissie did not enjoy rising at 6.30am every morning to read the Bible before breakfasting nearly two hours later, she did nevertheless enjoy the classes which followed. Geography, mental arithmetic, singing, drawing, general knowledge but above all she delighted in sewing, as she had a passion for clothes and fashion from an early age. Already she had sewn several flannel petticoats, cotton chemises, a linen pinafore, an apron, a comb bag and many hemmed pocket handkerchiefs throughout the year.

Now, however, Chrissie was in the process of modelling some garments she had not created. Before visiting her daughter, Betsy had ventured into Kennington and Jenner in Princes Street and had emerged much poorer but with two large bags. Chrissie had already opened one and had discovered a cage-like crinoline foundation made of fine steel hoops placed about three inches apart and supported by wide tapes. Chrissie was so excited, as she knew this to be the very latest fashion, and one which would make the wearing of many petticoats now unnecessary. She had already donned the contraption and was now slipping on a wide-skirted dress also found in the bag. The pale-blue and navy material of the dress almost matched the colour of the young girl's eyes, while the shape of the gown enhanced her willowy figure. At the sight of herself in her looking glass, Chrissie clapped her hands in sheer delight, causing her ringlets to bounce on either side of her head.

"Mama, dear Mama, thank you. Thank you so much. I couldn't have asked for a more perfect present. And it will go so well with the Paisley shawl Aunt Margaret gave me for my last birthday."

"And look what else I have for you, my dear."

Chrissie opened the other large bag and found a round flat-brimmed straw hat bedecked with a navy velvet ribbon to match the piping on the dress.

"Oh Mama, it's what I've been longing for ever since I saw pictures of Her Majesty dressed in one just like this. I'll look quite the lady in it."

"Yes, I was assured that these straw bonnets are all the rage and I knew it would suit you so well."

Hastily, Chrissie tried on the hat placing it well back on top of her head and tied the ribbon in a big bow beneath her chin. Then she ran to her mother and hugged her tightly.

"Don't spoil your hat, my dear. Watch you don't squash it."

Chrissie after a moment released her mother and again admired herself in the looking glass.

"You look the picture of perfection."

"Why don't you buy yourself one too, Mama? You would look splendid in a hat like this."

"Perhaps I shall. But now I know you can look quite the young lady when you visit your Aunt Margaret and Christina in Liverpool next month. It will also be useful for later when you visit Bellwood."

"Oh thank you, dear Mama. It is so kind of you to remember me. And now, did you visit the Grange Cemetery as you were planning to do?"

Betsy's uncle, Andrew Anderson, had died the previous year at the age of 75 at his home in Minto Street with his wife Georgina and two sons, John and Thomas, by his bedside.

"Yes, my dear. Since his death I have discovered more about him and, while I knew he had fought and survived the Napoleonic Wars in Naples, I only recently found out he had also served in five campaigns in Spain during that War, for which he was awarded a silver medal with five clasps."

"Do you remember all the stories he used to tell us of his times in the Wars?"

"Indeed I do, and I remember how your uncles, John, James and Thomas, loved hearing them too when they were growing up. It was rather strange to see James officiating as minister at his uncle's burial service."

"His life certainly seemed to have been so full of adventure."

"Yes, and tragedy too, unfortunately, what with both his first wife's death in Jamaica and then his daughter's more recently."

"Yes, that's true, Mama, but he was so happy with Aunt Georgina, as well as being so proud of his two sons. I suppose they are your cousins. What has happened to them anyway? Are they still in Edinburgh?"

"No. Thomas is now living in Aberdeen and is a Lieutenant Colonel in the 78th Highlanders while John is in Hong Kong, so poor Aunt Georgina is now living on her own in Minto Street. I do try and visit her when I can, but there is always so much to do when I come here."

"So that leaves only one of your four uncles alive, Mama. How is Uncle Archie anyway?"

"He's still as busy as ever with the nurseries and seems to be functioning remarkably well from what I hear, but he's so lucky to have your Uncle John there to help with the business and your Aunt Jessie to run Bellwood for him."

Betsy could not but be amazed at the change that had taken place in her sister over the years. She had been a saucy young madam, but was now a much revered and slightly frightening 'grande dame'. Andrew had never really liked her, although his strong dislike of yesteryear had mellowed.

"You do know that your Aunt Christina is still living nearby at Knowehead as she's looking after your cousins there since Aunt Alice died. Uncle James must be grateful to have her there. She and Lewis seem to be permanent fixtures there now."

Andrew had not been partial to this other sister-in-law, Christina Bilton, either, as she had always been somewhat bossy and had an answer for everything. Betsy wondered how James Miller, her poor widowed brother-in-law, was getting on with her in the house.

"And now I hear your Uncle James is helping young Lewis prepare to be a solicitor like himself. Lewis must be about 17 now."

"Does Lewis not want to go to sea like his father?"

"No, not as far as I know."

The family rarely saw Captain Bilton, as he was so often away at sea.

"But enough of what is happening in Scotland, young lady. Are you looking forward to visiting your Aunt Margaret and cousin Christina in Liverpool?"

"Of course, Mama. But why exactly have they gone down there?"

"Because Christina wishes to become a nurse and, other than St Thomas's in London, there is nowhere else for her to train. A certain Mr Rathbone, a wealthy merchant, has employed Miss Florence Nightingale no less to give instruction there and to set up a school on the same lines as the one she began in London. I think it is very brave of Margaret and Christina to move south to do so, and I wish them both well. Liverpool must be quite a challenge."

"Why so, Mama?"

"Because it is a large port and a dangerous place by all accounts. Many sailors come off the ships with all kinds of diseases, so it must be hard to be a nurse there. Anyway, they are both asking fondly after you. Christina in particular wants to know all about the school, having been a pupil here herself."

"Oh, I can tell her all about what's happened since she left. Mrs Bathgate came as headmistress after Christina left and has made many changes. By all accounts what we have now appears luxurious to what it was like in Christina's time."

The school still appeared to be lacking any luxury, thought Betsy, as she looked round the sparse, large dormitory in which they found themselves. This was, she had been told, one of three and provided sleeping accommodation for 24 girls. Next door were two small baths for 80 pupils, as bathing was only supposed to take place once a month. In between times there were 21 basins in which they would make their ablutions. She could well imagine this would not appeal to Chrissie, as she was used to sharing the manse with only her parents.

"Mama, what about the Selkirk crowd? Uncle Henry and Aunt Margaret? How are they getting on?"

"Well, your uncle is looking rather podgy. I believe he has been or is just about to be Provost of Selkirk. He's such a jovial man; I'm sure he will be very popular with the townspeople there."

"And the Jedburgh Andersons? What's happened there? I suppose they are all still at home with Aunt Eliza?"

Alexander had left his American wife to look after 9 children when he had died and Betsy guessed they were all still under the age of sixteen. Poor woman. Not only had she been uprooted from Hong Kong to come and live in Jedburgh, she had also suddenly become a widow left with all these children.

"Yes, I think so. I haven't seen Eliza for quite a while, but I'm sure she's coping with her brood."

"And what of Aunt Clara and Uncle Alexander? Did you stay with them last night in Rutland Square?"

"Yes, I did. It was good to see them again. Papa was sorry he could not accompany me this time, as he and your uncle enjoy each other's company so much. Uncle Alexander continues to work as hard as ever at his medical research, writing and lecturing – I believe his latest interest is in the treatment of drunkards. It is a real problem and causing a furore amongst both the medical and legal professions."

Betsy was not prepared to discuss the subject in detail but was only too well aware that alcohol was being consumed in enormous quantities throughout the land. She had been told that the population of Scotland aged 15 and over was drinking, on average, the equivalent of a little under a pint of duty-charged whisky a week. There was no legal restriction on who might buy drink, and drunkenness among quite young apprentices and women was taken for granted. Sadly too, from working with the mining families in the Avonbridge district, Betsy saw there was a definite link between drink and crime. Domestic violence and battered wives were part of the whisky culture. Both Andrew and Alexander, along with others in the Church and in medicine, were part of the ever growing moral crusade to control the drinking habits of the poor.

"Anyway, despite all this, your uncle has always been profoundly interested in our Church and has just been appointed medical adviser to the United Presbyterian Mission Board. Your Papa is delighted. Oh, he sends his love and wants to know about your education and especially how your religious studies are progressing."

Both mother and daughter laughed with affection as they talked of Andrew. His love for his only daughter was unbounded and his care for her spiritual well-being was of great importance to him.

"You can set his mind at rest, Mama. As well as our early morning readings of the Scriptures, we have prayers at night before retiring. On Friday evenings we even have scripture lessons for two hours and on Saturday mornings we take part in another two hours devoted to Bible reading, examination of Bible history and studies of the Shorter Catechism. Saturday evenings are dedicated to some more religious instruction, and of course on Sunday mornings we attend family worship. Do you think all that will satisfy Papa?"

Both smiled at each other for, while they appreciated the importance of the teachings of the Bible, they also knew there were other things that mattered such as clothes and fashion. Betsy was also concerned that her young daughter was being suitably nourished. Certainly, she looked fit and well, but she enquired as to what exactly the young ladies were being fed.

"Oh, Mama, do you really want to know?"

Betsy nodded and so after a long sigh, Chrissie began to list the menus.

"Every morning we have porridge and buttermilk for breakfast and at lunchtime a variety of food. Most weekdays it's broth, cold meat and potatoes, with Wednesday being the highlight of the week when we have roast beef or mutton. On Sunday, we usually have broth and beef in winter and curds and bread in summer. Then around late afternoon we have bread and milk and the same around 7pm. Now does that satisfy you, Mama?"

"And you are learning to cook as well as sew, I trust."

"Yes, but we're not expected to learn to cook family meals. It is presumed that, when we marry, we shall manage the household rather than be cooks ourselves. However, that is only dealt with in Class Four, our final year, when we shall learn how to prepare drinks and perhaps little delicacies for any sick members of a family.

Do not worry, Mama. We are being trained to be diligent wives and mothers, whose knowledge in running a household will be of paramount importance, but I only hope my future husband can afford a cook and several servants, otherwise my family will starve."

Already Betsy suspected her daughter was more interested in the comforts money could bring unlike her older cousin, Christina, who had chosen to dedicate herself to looking after the sick and ailing. She only hoped Chrissie would not be disappointed in her quest.

Then Betsy's eyes rested upon a pile of books by her daughter's bed. 'Butler's Spelling Book', 'The Old and New Testament Biography' and 'The Shorter Catechism'. These were books she remembered from her own childhood.

"Is that all you have to read? You must have a look at our library at home."

"When we are in the Fourth Class we study 'Macbeth' and 'Richard II'. Also, someone has mentioned 'Marmion', 'Bleak House' and 'Vanity Fair'. Have you heard of any of these, Mama?"

"Indeed I have. We even have a copy of 'Marmion' in the manse. I presume you know it was written by Sir Walter Scott. As for 'Bleak House', I read it in serial fashion in 'Household Words' some time ago. But I've yet to read 'Vanity Fair'."

Suddenly from downstairs the mighty gong was heard summoning the pupils to their usual late afternoon fare of bread and milk. It was four o'clock and time for Betsy to take her leave.

After an affectionate and slightly tearful farewell, Betsy descended the stairs, past the two lamps not as yet lit which stood at the entrance hall, and made her way out into a breezy March afternoon. Now she must steel herself to leave her favourite city and return to face the ugliness of the Slamannan plain. However, she had long ago committed herself to a life dedicated to helping her husband in his work, for she firmly believed God had a purpose for her in this life and she would fulfil it as best she could. With that in mind, she strode off down Archibald Place towards the station and home.

Chapter 4

1869: A Birthday

As the train raced on through the September countryside, Betsy looked up from her book and across to Andrew and Chrissie. She smiled as she watched her daughter gazing out of the window,

Meanwhile, her husband was studying some papers – no doubt some church business – and every now and again would nod his head in agreement with their contents. Poor Andrew. How he had aged over the last few years. Gone was the thick head of dark wavy hair, leaving a bald pate surrounded by a circle of fine white hair. His face, always thin and weathered, was now furrowed with many lines. However, those piercing enquiring blue eyes, which had always attracted her, were still very much alert, as was his quick and perceptive mind. She and Andrew had been married now for over twenty years and she was conscious that she too had changed over the years. The role of minister's wife had not been an easy one, for both she and Andrew had dedicated their lives to the good of the parishioners, and the physical and mental efforts had taken their toll.

While Andrew's stipend had doubled since they had arrived in Avonbridge all these years ago, it had provided little luxury compared with that enjoyed by most of her brothers and sisters.

However, Betsy felt she had little to complain about for she was still alive and well, as were Andrew and Chrissie, which was more than could be said of some of her siblings and their families, not to mention the plight of many of their poor parishioners back in Slamannan.

Clever businessmen like her Uncle Archie were certainly working hard to make the country successful and they had become prosperous. However, others, who also toiled hard, were not so lucky. Workers such as the miners of Slamannan, who toiled day and night to provide coal for the nation, as well as those who were building rail tracks such as those on which her train was now running, had also done their share of the work to make Britain become the most powerful country in the world. Yet their rewards were nothing compared with those of the businessmen involved in the venture.

As the train journeyed onwards, Betsy began to recall the happy few days she and Andrew had recently spent in London on their visit to the Great Exhibition held in the Crystal Palace. There Britain's technical achievements and many inventions had been displayed to the rest of the world. There she had seen the wonder of cotton spinning machines, steam hammers, locomotives, telegraphs, steam turbines, printing machines and scientific instruments. Both she and Andrew had been overwhelmed by what they had witnessed. She particularly remembered seeing the 24-ton lump of coal that greeted every visitor at the entrance to the Crystal Palace, a reminder to all that it was coal that fed the furnaces of the Industrial Age; coal that fuelled the engines and the locomotives; and coal that powered the steam trains, one of the greatest inventions of the age, as she had so often been told when growing up in Greenock where its inventor, James Watt, had been born.

She had been so struck by the importance of industry in people's lives that, when she read 'Little Dorrit' by her favourite writer Charles Dickens, she had carefully memorised the words of one of the characters in the book. "Keep always at it and I'll keep you always at it and you keep someone else always at it. This is the whole duty of man in a commercial country."

Many families had made colossal fortunes from the profits of these industries and the solid ranks of the middle classes had become prosperous, but Betsy had also heard Andrew state that 70% of the population – about a million people – belonging to either the 'lower skilled' or 'unskilled' categories were working for a wage of below £50 a year. She heard daily news of people moving to live over the Border into England, as the average wage there was 10% higher and with lower living costs. Many more chose to say goodbye to their friends and families forever and go abroad to live in Canada, America or Australia.

Andrew was now reading 'The Scotsman' and catching up on all the news both local and from further afield. He was a caring man, but also one who expected high standards of behaviour from his family and his flock. He, like the rest of the clergy, was regarded as being a social and intellectual leader of the community, his role being to encourage parishioners to abide by their religious duty. He, like many others, was driven by a religious vision which equated social improvement with moral improvement, and believed in the value of hard work, self-help, thrift and temperance. While Betsy firmly believed in that too, she was also aware that it was easy for the largely upper middle class eldership of the congregation to lecture to the poor. She also found it ironic that it was the members of the working class who did the highest percentage of churchgoing.

But today, Betsy decided to forget about life at home and enjoy this visit to Perth. Andrew had now stopped reading and was winking at her from behind his spectacles for soon they would be going through the Moncrieff Hill tunnel and she knew what the significance of the wink conveyed. The Queen and her family had travelled through it in 1850 on a visit to Scotland and had been greeted by a royal salute given by Uncle Archie's two cannons which stood in front of Bellwood House. They were part of the Kinnoull Hill Rock Artillery Company's arsenal of weaponry intended to protect the river approach to Perth. Her uncle had thought it appropriate to welcome the royal guests by firing the cannons, just as he had also done to celebrate the opening of the Tay Railway Bridge in 1847.

She then felt Chrissie clutching her arm affectionately, for she too was sharing the same thought. They all knew how proud the old man was of his armoury. Now they were on their way to celebrate his 80th birthday.

Once through the tunnel with no explosions greeting them, they found themselves at the station where David Menzies, the Bellwood House coach driver who had held the post for over 20 years, was waiting to take them to join the other family members. They always enjoyed their visits to Perth, renowned now for its manufacturing of writing inks, timber, coal, blue slate, leather and flax.

That very day, being Friday, it was market day and the local farmers were mingling while the Irish drovers were standing about waiting for a job to drive the cattle to their new quarters. Betsy took in all the sights and sounds as the brougham approached its destination. She loved this town with its shops in South Street and elsewhere, so often visited by her and her sisters over the years.

Soon they were crossing the bridge over the River Tay and facing Kinnoull Hill where, after turning right, they were greeted by the familiar wide 32-acre expanse of the Dickson and Turnbull Nurseries. The dark green pines clothed the sides and summit of Kinnoull Hill along with conifers, ornamental shrubs, deciduous trees, rhododendrons, herbaceous and alpines, roses and orchids. Here, the nurseries had managed to cultivate the Scotch rose from seed and she remembered her uncle had been particularly proud of one he had named, the Scarlet Hawthorn. There, in the middle of all this luxuriant growth, stood Bellwood House itself.

Menzies stopped the brougham at the front door, where Jessie Turner was already there waiting to greet them. Betsy never failed to remember that this younger sister had once been a flighty, gossipy young lady for whom Andrew had little time. Now she was the stately, cultured and revered chatelaine of Bellwood, a widow of long-standing who had turned into a hard-working and extremely prosperous businesswoman and farmer. Now she appeared quite formidable to all who knew her and even Betsy, around 10 years her senior, was somewhat in awe of her.

Jessie stood at the imposing entrance to the house with John, their brother. Now in his late fifties, he still looked fit and full of energy. Alongside them was Margaret, her older sister, who was now staying in Perth permanently. Betsy was somewhat taken aback at her appearance, as she seemed to have aged considerably. She seemed smaller and frailer than the last time Betsy had seen her but then her life had not been easy for, only three years previously, her only daughter, Christina, had been buried in Kinnoull graveyard. In spite of her father's lifelong work in preventing cholera in the Gorbals, she had succumbed to the dreaded disease and had died at the age of 30.

Betsy watched Chrissie, after having greeted her Aunt Jessie and Uncle John, as she turned to her Aunt Margaret and to whom she gave an especially affectionate hug. Chrissie had often stayed with her aunt and her cousin, Christina, over the years wherever they were living at the time and, despite there being 12 years' difference in age between the two cousins, Chrissie had always viewed Christina as a kind of role model. But now there was no Christina to meet her, and her absence was particularly noticeable at a time like this when the family came together.

However, today was a time of happiness and Jessie ushered Betsy into the house while John whisked Andrew and Chrissie away to the nursery to seek out the old man whose birthday they had all come to celebrate. Chrissie had always been a favourite relative of his, for she had visited and read to him many times over the years as his eyesight began growing weaker. Betsy remembered Andrew's advice given in one of his letters to his daughter about "improving her elocution and her lungs for distinct and easily intelligible reading to her great uncle." Uncle Archie had indeed appreciated Chrissie's clear, well-articulated voice and had enjoyed listening to her reading such things as the serialised stories of Charles Dickens in 'Household Words', and the local news in 'The Perthshire Courier'. Chrissie had joked with her mother that, now Tolstoy's 'War and Peace' had just been published, her next reading aloud task might be to tackle such a tome. However, there would be no time for such an undertaking that weekend.

Before following her sisters into the house, Betsy glanced up at the four-storied building with its 22 rooms, a far cry from the manse at Avonbridge despite its recent renovations. She then went inside and across the hall to the wide staircase which led to her bedroom. This house she knew so well, having stayed there many times, and had witnessed the many changes that had taken place over the years. She made her way up the staircase, passing the portraits of various members of the Dickson and Turnbull families who seemed to be staring out at her from their heavy, gilded frames. There were the Dickson sons of the original Archibald, along with other portraits of members of their large family, but none of the Turnbull family for they could not have afforded such likenesses to be made. What would these ancestors be thinking of all this, wondered Betsy, as she made her way up the staircase?

Soon she was back in the comfortable bedroom to which she was usually assigned with its familiar wardrobe, chaise longue, chest of drawers and looking glass on the dressing room table. She began to feel tired and so made her way to the heavily carved large four-poster bed with its plush curtains, deep pillows and eiderdown, and sat down. She wanted to curl up and go to sleep there, but she knew she must soon go downstairs and join the ladies in the drawing room. All her sisters would be there and would be waiting to take tea with her and to catch up on all the news.

Before doing so, Betsy took a moment to enjoy the peace of the room with its view over the river and town. What a luxury to sit and do nothing. Would she have preferred to be living in these more comfortable circumstances, sheltered from the harsh realities and ugliness of poverty? Perhaps so, perhaps not. But now she must make a concentrated effort in taking off her bonnet and shawl, tidying her hair in front of the looking glass and smoothing down her skirt. Very soon she was ready to go downstairs to join the ladies.

As she entered the drawing room, her three sisters came forward to greet her. With Jessie and Margaret was her third sister, Christina, now too living in Perth at Knowehead House with the Miller family. Alice had produced three sons and one daughter before she had died and now Christina was helping James look after them. Her own son, Lewis, now a 25-year-old fully-qualified lawyer, also lived with them, and Betsy knew that at least one if not two of the Miller boys was also planning to follow in their father's footsteps and also make a career in law.

And so, on that afternoon, around the large round table in the drawing room, the company sat. It consisted of the four Anderson sisters with Mary, their brother John's wife, a pleasant and motherly lady of whom Betsy had always been fond. Meanwhile outside, John was taking Andrew and Chrissie to meet Uncle Archie. Their youngest brother, Thomas, would be joining them later from Bridge of Allan. Sadly, however, their middle and unmarried brother, James, who had for many years been a minister in the village of Norham in the north of England and who had officiated at both their Uncle Andrew's and Christina's funerals, had himself recently passed away at Bellwood. Betsy knew that, while all the family missed him, it was her husband, Andrew, who particularly missed his company for both had been ministers of the United Presbyterian Church and, in spite of being on either side of the Border, they had always had much to discuss when they had got together. Alice, her youngest sister and her niece, Christina Leech, were also of course missing from this family gathering.

Enough of these sad thoughts. Betsy had always admired this room with its flocked wallpaper and little miniatures hanging on its walls, plus its welcoming red carpet on which sat the high-backed velvet chairs and large round table set for afternoon tea. Now, she welcomed the reassuring sound of the swish of taffetas and silks of the dresses and the scent of eau de cologne worn by the ladies. After a warm welcome and the usual greetings from everyone, she then proceeded to join the company round the table with its white tablecloth and fine china tea set. Jessie then began to pour the tea from the famous Dickson silver tea pot with its long swan-like neck and simple, classical Georgian lines made for their great-uncle, William, who in turn had left it to their Uncle Archie along with the nursery and house.

While handing round the cups and saucers, Jessie said "How wonderful it is to have you with us for the birthday celebrations, my dear. It's going to be quite a turn out for the dinner this evening, for nearly all the family will be present, and tomorrow a ball is planned for all the neighbours to come and join us."

"Why, Jessie, it is such a pleasure to be here," agreed Betsy. "I just hope I've brought all the appropriate attire for such a grand occasion. Am I acquainted with any of the neighbours who will be attending?"

"We have just been discussing our near neighbours, the Grays of Bowerswell House," chipped in her other sister, Christina. "You know them. You must remember all the fuss that was made over their daughter, Effie, when she married Mr Ruskin."

"I certainly do remember it for Andrew and I were married in the same year, but everyone seemed to be talking about the Ruskin wedding."

"Yes. They were married at home in Bowerswell," added Mary. "I attended with John and Uncle Archibald, although it was mainly a quiet family affair."

"The wedding may have been quiet, but the later annulment had the world talking," interjected Christina. She had always delighted in scandal and Betsy knew this news must have kept her sister entertained for days. "And now here we are some 20 years later with Effie now married to the artist, John Everett Millais, and mother to many children."

Before Christina could convey any more gossip, Jessie added, "They're up from London at the moment and staying here at Annat Lodge, next to the Gray's house. As you know, they always come for the summer and should be with us tomorrow evening for the ball."

"But will Sophie, Effie's younger sister, be with us? She's a funny one." Christina raised one eyebrow and gave them all a quizzical look.

"Christina, what are you insinuating?" Betsy laughed, knowing well how much Christina loved intrigue.

"Come, Christina," interrupted Margaret, "Your suspicions are only based on servants' 'tittle tattle'. We should feel sorry for Sophie if she is unwell."

"Unwell? Why, word has it that she is not eating and is very thin and depressed. I heard that all she does is play the piano day and night. Did you know she was sent away to London by her parents to get some treatment?"

Again, to take their minds off the subject of Sophie, Jessie said, "Effie is now in her late forties, but of course she still has younger brothers who are not married."

Then again Christina felt she had to supply more information for the uninitiated, although all those round the table already knew what she was about to say.

"Effie's mother, Mrs Gray, has had 23 children, would you credit that?" Christina's eyes opened wide.

"Enough of all this gossip," said Jessie handing round the shortbread. "And you must be kind to the family, for they have suffered many infant deaths along the way."

Mary then spoke. "I should love to see Mr Millais' triple portrait of their three daughters which is now on display in London. It's called 'Three Sisters' and depicts Effie, Mary and Carrie in muslin frocks, blue bows and blonde ringlets. I'm sure it's enchanting as they are such three lovely little girls and he does paint children so well."

Then turning to Betsy, Mary enquired politely after Betsy

and life in Slamannan. However there was little to recount for Betsy knew her sisters would not be interested in the misery and heartaches of the people there. "More importantly, has Chrissie got a beau yet?" enquired Christina.

"Not as far as I know, but she does enjoy reading romances and even writes poetry herself. I'm sure there must be someone on her mind but she tells us so little."

Betsy remembered that only the other day she had come across an Acrostic poem lying on her daughter's bed but, try as she might, she could not work out the name. Soon all this small talk came to an end, for it was time for the ladies to retire to their rooms in order to prepare for the evening. Some 20 people in the family were to attend and Betsy only hoped she would remember who was who, for her sisters could get easily offended if one identified their offspring incorrectly.

A few hours later, in a heavy silk mauve crinoline with her deep purple shawl round her shoulders and crocheted fingerless mitts on her hands, Betsy made her way downstairs. She was accompanied by Andrew in his black frock coat, high starched collar and bow tie and to Betsy was as tall and handsome as ever. However, it was Chrissie who was the star attraction. The 20-year-old had grown into a very attractive young lady and, dressed in a white crinoline gown with its fashionable deep décolleté neckline showing off her sloping shoulders and hour-glass figure, she was greeted by many an admiring glance. Her young, heart-shaped face expressed sheer joy and excitement, inviting all around her to feel the same way.

Amid all the laughter and chatter, Betsy heard someone playing and singing 'Where're You Walk' and, through the crowd, she thought she saw her youngest sister, Alice, sitting at the piano. But, of course, it was not, for Alice had died years ago. Instead it was her sister's daughter, also called Alice. She was about the same age as Chrissie and, on seeing her cousin, she suddenly stopped playing, stood up and rushed over to welcome her, to be followed immediately by other young Andersons, Biltons and Miller family members. Meanwhile, Betsy tried hard to remember who was who. These nephews and nieces of hers had grown up so fast. It did not seem so long ago since they were little children running around in the garden playing games, but now they had grown up into attractive and totally unrecognisable young gentlemen and ladies.

The gong then sounded, inviting the party to make their way to the dining room. As she moved towards the door, while taking her brother John's arm, Betsy was struck by the luxury of the candlelit room with its numerous large mirrors on either wall reflecting the long-dropped silver chandeliers above which shone down on the heavily-decked dining table. Its epergne of flowers, fruits and candles branched out across the centre, while the cutlery and crystal glasses gleamed. Each place setting was accompanied by a name card and carefully-folded napkin. On one side of the room sat the tureens, assiettes and decanters on the sideboard, all ready to be served by the staff standing by.

It took a few minutes before everyone had located their seats. Of the young people, there appeared to be far more men and boys than women: three Miller boys – James, Archibald and George; four Anderson boys – George, Alexander, Archie and Andrew and Lewis Bilton. Quickly reminding herself of the names, Betsy thought how easy it would be to mix them up for the names James, John, Andrew, George and Thomas had been repeated down the generations. As for the young ladies there were only two of them that evening, her niece, Alice Miller, and her own daughter, Chrissie. As for her own generation, Betsy's brother John, with his wife, Mary, were surprisingly the only couple there other than herself and Andrew, for James Miller was a widower now Alice was dead, Christina's husband was at sea, Margaret's husband was in Glasgow, and Thomas, their youngest brother, was present but single.

Then through the door came the chatelaine herself, Jessie Turner, accompanying the star of the evening, Uncle Archie. While Jessie made her way to one end of the table, Uncle Archie was helped to the other but, despite his 80 years, he was still a gentleman of considerable presence, with his white mutton-chop sideburns and moustache. Under his white bushy eyebrows, his eyes twinkled with joy as he took in all those around him. No doubt he knew who everyone was, thought Betsy. He might be an octogenarian, but he was still sprightly in body and mind, and one who could still conduct himself successfully in business.

Betsy found herself seated between her brother-in-law, James Miller, and her 16-year-old nephew, George Anderson, and as she looked round the table at the guests, she realised that all there that evening, apart from their partners, were either the children or grandchildren of George and Christy Anderson. She almost smiled, knowing how proud her mother would have been to see such an assembly in such a luxurious setting.

As the meal progressed, the conversation went from talk about 'The People's Friend', the new publication by D.C. Thompson's in Dundee, to the subject of Charles Dickens' visit to Edinburgh earlier that year in May when he delivered his 'Farewell Read-ings' at the Music Hall in George Street. Although unwell, he had finally managed to give an animated rendition of the scene in 'Oliver Twist' where Sykes had killed Nancy. He had then finished with a dramatic reading of his 'Christmas Carol'. Chris-tina proudly announced that she and her son, Lewis, had been at the occasion. She then proceeded to give a very moving account of the whole affair, adding there was not a dry eye in the house by the end of the evening. Talk on the use of gas lighting soon followed, but discussion of the last fully public hanging in Scot-land in Perth the previous year was quickly squashed, the subject being deemed not fit for the dinner table and certainly not for such a happy occasion.

After the meal, while they nibbled sweetmeats and sipped their drinks, it was time for the speeches and who better to conduct the proceedings than John, having worked at the nursery for so many years? He therefore proudly stood up beside his uncle and addressed the assembly. Everyone, of course, knew the facts about Archibald Turnbull's life but were nonetheless happy to hear the story again, beginning with his birth in Greenhouse in the Borders, to his arrival in Perth in 1803 to help his unmarried uncle, William Dickson, with the work in the Perth Nurseries. When his uncle passed away in 1835, the business had become an extremely profitable enterprise. Uncle Archie took over and then went on to extend the nursery grounds in the parish of Kinnoull. John also mentioned that, while doing so, Uncle Archie had also been busy serving the people of Perth in other ways by holding a seat on Perth's Council Board, where he had more than once been referred to as the last survivor of 'the beautiful order'. He was also a Justice of the Peace as well as the original promoter of the Perthshire Horticultural Society. As if that were not enough, having been a staunch supporter of the City of Perth's Conservative Association, he had also been its President for many years.

Then came the part of his Uncle's story known by all but still very much enjoyed, in which John himself had figured.

"Two years ago, we had a visit from none other than the famous Charles Darwin seeking information from our illustrious uncle, who was that day unfortunately away on business. I therefore had the pleasure of meeting the great man and together we discussed the blotched Breadalbane Ash, along with other things."

Having heard the story many times, some of the young men at the table were unsubtly yawning, but this did not perturb John from continuing to describe how he and Mr Darwin had discussed the inoculation of disease by budding. This had obviously been one of John's proudest moments and all in the company allowed him his moment of glory.

Eventually he asked the assembled company to be upstanding and to toast Uncle Archie on his eightieth birthday, while wishing him many more years of happiness and prosperity to come. The old gentleman then got to his feet and thanked everyone, finally reminding them that the celebrations were not yet over, for on the following evening there was to be a ball held in the ballroom to which they were all invited. He hoped everyone would dance the night away, as he himself fully intended to do.

So stood the last of Betsy's four uncles, the other three, James Turnbull, her mother's brother, and Thomas and Andrew Anderson, her father's brothers, now all having passed away. However, here stood her Uncle Archie, still seeming fit to live a few more years yet, as he indeed did.

Chapter 5

1876: An End of an Era

The biting cold October wind tugged at Betsy's black bombazine skirt as she held onto her hat with one hand and clutched her handbag with the other. She turned at the gate of the manse and looked back at what had been her home for nearly 30 years.

But now it was her home no longer, for Andrew had died that summer. He had not been well for several years and, on the very evening his application had been admitted as an annuitant on the Aged and Infirm Ministers' Fund and was being considered, he had a heart attack and died soon after. Now he lay in the graveyard in Bathgate under a most imposing, obelisk gravestone erected by the kind congregation and friends of the Avonbridge Church. Engraved on it, along with his name and details, were the words "Waiting for the coming of the Lord Jesus Christ".

'The Falkirk Herald', in announcing his death, had referred to him as "one of the noblest and most respected of the ministers connected with the Falkirk Presbytery "and went on to say "He was a strong-brained man, and a man of large and theological attainment – an assiduous student, an able preacher, a conscientious pastor, a man of shrewd sense and ready humour and a genial Christian. He was a modest man, and his brethren who knew him best admired him most." She could not disagree with that and knew he was genuinely much missed by many, no more so than by herself.

Life as his wife had certainly been a challenge, not easy, but always worthwhile. They were both devout Christians committed to helping the people of Avonbridge, both practically and spiritually. The population had grown over the years and life had been both good and bad for their parishioners. There had certainly been moments to celebrate, but more often there were times of extreme hardship. Betsy had thanked God daily to have been spared a life such as those she saw around her, where many people could barely scrape enough together to exist.

Andrew's stipend had not been a great deal but with the rent on his property of Hillhead Farm near Lilliesleaf of £70 a year together with the interest on Uncle Archie's legacy wisely invested in the growing railway network, they managed. This allowed them to employ one servant to help with the daily chores, first Isabella Morton, then Mary Oswell and latterly Betsy Flemington. All of them had proved to be committed workers attending to the usual cooking and constant mending of clothes, be it the turning of heels on socks and stockings or the darning of sheets. Meanwhile, Betsy had sat on committees to aid the less fortunate and, with the help of Chrissie as she grew older, had also helped the miners' wives with their babies and children. This left little time to play the piano, write letters and sew samplers in the evenings, but even these activities she somehow managed to succeed in doing between entertaining Andrew's colleagues, their own friends and family.

Now, however, there was no home left. The manse only theirs while Andrew was minister and so, for the last few months, she had had been employed in getting rid of many of their belongings, while at the same time making sure the letters, books and various pieces of furniture she cherished would come with her to her new home. She had kept the rosewood worktable with its pink silk plaited basket, Andrew's games table on which he had spent many happy nights playing chess with friends and family, his treasured card case presented to him by the congregation, the silver candlesticks, the wine holders and the monogrammed cutlery which had belonged to the Dickson family, as well as her Uncle James Turnbull's snuff box.

As she stared up at the house, happy memories came flooding back and, as she stood on the doorstep, she fondly remembered the day Andrew had heroically lifted her over it when they had first arrived on their wedding day in 1847.

Through Andrew's study window, she pictured him once again sitting at his desk in the flicker of candlelight, engrossed in short-sightedly peering through his spectacles in complete concentration as he read or wrote a letter, or perhaps prepared a sermon, his earmarked bible always by his side. She remembered how pleased he was when the law had been passed entitling all children in Scotland between the ages of five and 13 to free education. Then, a couple of years later, he rejoiced once more when patronage in the Church of Scotland was abolished.

On turning to the drawing room window, Betsy began to imagine she could distinguish familiar faces from the past. There were her brothers and sisters, their spouses and children — the Turners, the Andersons, the Biltons, the Millers, and the Leechs. In one corner stood her brother, John, with his wife, Mary, chatting to her other brother, James, the one-time vicar from the north of England, while in another corner was her sister, Christina Bilton, with her little boy, Lewis, in conversation with her older sister, Margaret Leech, and her young daughter, Christina. Then her youngest sister, Alice Miller, entered the room with her husband, James, and their young family as they made their way to greet her other sister, Jessie Turner, who was accompanying their favourite uncle, Archie. While she was fond of all of her other uncles, Andrew in Edinburgh, Thomas in Selkirk and James in Roxburghshire, it was this uncle from Perth who had always held a special place in her heart, and no matter his age he had always been the attentive and interested businessman to the end.

As the rain began to fall, Betsy was brought back to the present day for now she remembered Uncle Archie was dead, having passed away the previous year at the age of 87. His funeral had been a particularly sad occasion for everyone in the family had gathered in Perth that day to mourn the old man's death. His funeral also brought back memories of another gathering, this time in Selkirk, when the Anderson family had gathered to celebrate the life of another ancestor. It was the inauguration service dedicated to the life of Mungo Park and a statue of him had been erected in front of the Dovecote. Betsy remembered how her old Uncle Andrew, her father's brother and the only one left of that generation of Andersons, had shed a tear as he had read the dedication to his older brother, Alexander, who had also died on that fatal journey to Africa. He would have been the only one present at that ceremony to have known the two heroes. Betsy herself, like all the other relations, had been brought up on stories of their adventures and she was almost certain that in every Anderson house a miniature of Mungo Park would be hanging on the wall, while a copy of 'Life and Travels of Mungo Park in Africa' would be sitting on a bookshelf. Yes, no one else there that day would have known the explorer other than Uncle Andrew, and he would have had his own private memories of their childhood long ago.

This inauguration had happened in 1859 and had been organised by her much-loved cousin, Dr Henry Scott Anderson, another of Park's nephews, his father, Dr Thomas Anderson, being the explorer's youngest brother-in-law. Having been provost of the burgh several times, Henry had put much energy into improving the town's street lighting, drainage and water supply, but it would always be the erection of his uncle's statue which was to give him most pride. Otherwise, he spent much of his time on his favourite hobby of fox-hunting and was a regular follower of the Duke of Buccleuch's hounds. While enjoying life to the utmost, he and his wife Margaret, now living at the Dovecote, the old Anderson home, shared a great sadness for they no longer had any children. Their little son, Thomas, had died in childhood and their daughter Jessie, although alive on the day of the statue ceremony, had later died at 16. In memory of these two children, Henry had recently erected a beautiful window to them both in Selkirk Parish Church.

Of course, Henry and Margaret had been frequent visitors to the manse as had his brothers and sisters, although his oldest brother, Alexander, had not lived long in Scotland, having returned from Hong Kong, before dying. But their young sister, Clara, did visit often with her husband, Dr Alexander Peddie, and their children.

But as for the Park family itself, her Aunt Allie, Uncle Mungo's widow, was long dead as were all her children: Mungo, an Assistant Surgeon with the East India Company, dying in Madras in 1823; Thomas in East Africa while searching for information on his father's death; and Archibald, a colonel in the Bengal army, who died in 1867. Archibald had not even been born when his father had left Peebles for Africa. Their only sister, Elizabeth, who had married and had lived in Wales with her family, was now also dead.

All these people had spent many fine times together in the manse. Betsy could still hear Henry's loud guffaws followed by the usual laughter from those around, while the murmurings of quiet conversations could be heard taking place in corners or over the games table where Alexander Peddie and Andrew were playing. Animated gossip between the ladies as they sat sewing samplers or drinking tea could also be made out sometimes, disturbed by the clashing of pots and pans coming from the kitchen as Isabella, Mary or Betsy set to work. Throughout it all, Betsy began to imagine she could hear in the background the playing of the piano, and then the sight of her own young daughter, Chrissie, sitting on the piano stool, began to emerge, her ringlets bouncing to the music while she peered intently at the sheets of music on the stand before her. Could Betsy actually hear the strains of 'The Blue Danube' once more?

Thoughts of her daughter then drew Betsy's attention to a particular window above on the first floor. It had been Chrissie's bedroom. There her daughter had grown from a being a precious little baby to a fine young lady. There she had slept and dreamed, studied and played, and Betsy once again could see the books in the bookcase, holding the tales of 'Alice in Wonderland' as well as those by Hans Christian Andersen. Novels by Mr Dickens were of course also there beside those of the Bronte sisters. Chrissie had delighted in 'Wuthering Heights' in particular. Poetry also held a place in her heart, and she had even taken time to memorise some of the immortal lines of Mr Wordsworth and Mr Coleridge. At once stage, she had even been known to attempt to write her own.

But now Chrissie was a married woman, having four years before set out on her father's arm towards his church, where he had proudly officiated at her wedding. Betsy could easily picture her daughter again on the day, dressed in a gown of cream silk and satin with its ribbon bows on the bodice and with its polonaise overskirt which had attracted many gasps of appreciation from the guests. Her lifelong friend and cousin, Alice Miller, as her bridesmaid, had been at her side together with her other cousin, Lewis Bilton, now an upright young lawyer, who had officiated as best man to the groom, Allan Waugh.

Allan came from nearby Torphichen, and was already a successful seed merchant, having procured Craigend Mill in Avonbridge as well as land on which to build their dream house. He also owned Linmill Cottage in Torphichen where he had been brought up and where some of his family still lived. His mother was already dead but his father and brothers and sisters had attended the wedding. Betsy could not but keep a smile from her face as she could imagine her own mother's utter joy on her granddaughter making such a match.

After the September wedding, Chrissie and Allan had spent their honeymoon touring Europe and beyond and, on returning to Avonbridge, had settled into their newly built home, Craigbank

House. It boasted 16 rooms, several bathrooms with hot and cold water, a tennis court, a kitchen garden and stables for the carriage horses, as well as having stores in the grounds in which to store grain. Chrissie had always dreamed of a house of such splendour and now she had achieved her ambition by becoming the wife of 'a man of means'.

And yet, to Betsy, something did not seem quite right. She could not work out what triggered this doubt, but as soon as it appeared she dismissed it for Chrissie's happiness was paramount. Betsy knew that her lively young daughter had always been much impressed by wealth and her choice of husband would help her live the lifestyle she had always dreamed of having. Certainly Chrissie would want for nothing and yet…

The following April, Betsy's first grandchild, Elizabeth Marion Waugh, was born. By some mistake, her birth certificate gave her name as Christian until it had to be pointed out to Allan, who had made the mistake, that the baby should be called after her grandmother and not her mother. The mistake was quickly rectified and she was called after Betsy, as was proper. However, tragedy struck in the October of 1874, for this precious little daughter took ill suddenly and died.

However, at the end of that same year the couple were blessed with the arrival of another daughter, this time called Jessie, after Chrissie's aunt Jessie Turner in Perth, and this little girl lived and brought much cheer to the family. Now, not two years later, another baby was due and Betsy knew the parents were secretly praying for a boy to inherit the business.

Betsy sighed, for the old ways had to make way for the new. Now it was time for her to say farewell to the past and to the manse. It was time to leave the past and face the future, by going to live at Craigbank House with the Waugh family. No longer would she be the minister's wife but the mother-in-law and grandmother. No longer would conversations centre round the church and the parishioners, but would concentrate on mills and quarries, flax and stones or indeed on babies and houses. Betsy hoped her daughter's married life would be as happy as her own and, although hers could never have been called one of passion, it had always been one of mutual respect and support. Now she was sorely missing her greatest companion.

She turned her back for the last time on the manse, for it was time for the next minister of Avonbridge United Presbyterian Church, Rev. Hugh McMillan, to arrive with his family. And so she made her way reluctantly down the path to the carriage which would take her to her new home and to the next chapter in her life.

Part 5

Chrissie's Story

Chapter 1

1877: A Photograph

"Please hold your daughter still, if you will, Mrs Waugh," called Mr Henderson from under his little tent, while he tried to capture the photograph of his subjects.

Chrissie clutched Jessie tightly but the three-year old sitting on her knee was getting extremely bored. While the little girl was dressed for the occasion in a muslin white dress with wide short sleeves, and scarlet sash round her chubby waist to match her little red shoes, her mother, in contrast, wore the sombre black of mourning. Chrissie's father had died the previous June and, as etiquette dictated, she would be in mourning for a few months yet.

It was a raw March day and, on glancing out of Mr Henderson's studio window, Chrissie saw the tree branches being tossed by the wind against the backdrop of a steely grey sky. Apart from Jessie, everything in her life at that moment appeared bleak and depressing.

Here she was in Perth once more, having received a letter from her cousin, Alice, the previous week inviting her to come and visit. Chrissie had not seen Alice since her father's funeral, and so readily accepted the invitation. Her mother, Betsy, now permanently living with them at Craigbank, agreed to look after Chrissie's other daughter, 10-month-old Alice, to allow her and Jessie make the journey. But there was one condition. Chrissie and Jessie must have their photograph taken by Mr Henderson while on their visit to Perth.

Chrissie was keen to be with her cousin again, who was at that moment patiently sitting in the corner of the studio watching the procedure. Unlike Chrissie, she had not married and was still living at Knowehead House in Kinnoull with her father and brothers. The cousins had always been great friends and, despite the physical distance between them, had shared so many interests during their childhood, including the reading of novels such as 'The Moonstone' and 'The Woman in White' by Wilkie Collins. Their favourite, however, had been the best seller 'East Lynne', the tragic story of infidelities and double identities, recounting the plight of poor Lady Isabel Carlyle and her disfigurement. The book had made the girls weep and, when it came to the death of the lady's child, it had almost been too much for them to bear.

They had also taken a great interest in reading the works of John Ruskin, largely because of his connection to the Gray family, the neighbours of Bellwood. Like everyone else in the family, the girls were well aware of the events of Ruskin's marriage to Effie Gray and they found to their amusement that in 'Sesame and Lilies', he had addressed middle-class women as "Lilies of the Queen's Gardens". He also insisted that there were two separate spheres allotted by God to the two sexes, and that of the woman was none other than that of wifely duty. The cousins had been so intrigued by his words that, not only did they giggle at them, but had made a point of learning them by heart in order to quote them to each other at every available opportunity. They were also most amused by his description of a woman's place, "where man may bow before the myrtle throne and stainless sceptre of womanhood but, in return for being protected from all danger and temptation, she must in all things hold herself in subjection to her King." How pleased the cousins had been when Effie had escaped the clutches of the author and had married the more attractive Mr Millais.

While being aware of such quotations, they were much more in sympathy with the sentiments expressed by other writers such as the Bronte sisters, especially in 'The Tenant of Wildfell Hall' and 'Shirley'. Chrissie and Alice were fascinated by the injustices of society expressed in these novels, where men could go out and work in professions while "their sisters have no earthly employment but household work and sewing, stuck at home in tedium, their minds and views shrinking to wondrous narrowness." The cousins only had to examine their own lives to be well aware of the unfairness of the situation, for Alice's brothers were being given the opportunity to work and train to become lawyers while there had been no such opportunity offered to her.

Alice now 27 was still single with little hope of marrying for at that age she was already considered an 'old maid'. She had stayed at home, looked after her father and brothers, and seemed destined to keep house for them for good. She also fulfilled the role demanded of a single lady in such circumstances by playing the piano at social functions and churning out endless samplers, embroidered pictures, sofa cushions, footstools, table covers and tray cloths.

Meanwhile Chrissie had chosen to marry, despite Ruskin's words, having always yearned to be in charge of a rich mansion. As a child she had been taken by her mother to visit Christian Dickson, a cousin of her grandmother, Christy Anderson, at the large and impressive Hassendeanburn House which she had inherited from her brother. She had no need to marry. There the dowager had lived alone, save a lady's companion, a housemaid, a cook, a laundry maid, a gardener and a groom, until she had died in 1872, the same year Chrissie had married. The house was then left to her great nephew, a Colonel Archibald Dickson who, it was rumoured, was now in the process of making it into an even more splendid mansion. Chrissie had also been impressed to learn that the old lady had given £4000 to the Edinburgh Royal

Infirmary, £3000 to the Indigent Gentleman's Fund and £400 to the poor.

Having always been impressed by riches and, realising no one would be leaving Christian Dodds such a legacy, she knew she would have to marry someone wealthy. And so, when the successful 30-year-old mill owner from Torphichen, Allan Waugh, proposed marriage to her, vowing he would build her a wonderful mansion, she readily accepted.

Now she was indeed mistress of the splendid Craigbank House in Avonbridge and had also taken on the expected role of wife and mother. Now she had become exactly what Ruskin has described what a woman should be. Now she was "the angel in the house", expected to devote her life to her husband and to be submissive to his desires. the very role both she and Alice had once despised. Now she was learning to play the part of the perfect wife, passive and powerless, pious and pure, sympathetic and self-sacrificing as well as meek, charming and eternally grateful. But surely this was a small price to pay.

However, during the following four years, life had not been too kind to her. She had suffered the death of her first-born and then less than a year later her father had passed away. For this, she was now in mourning clothes.

Thanks to the death of Prince Albert in 1861, and the Queen's deep distress in losing him, mourning had become big business. Magazines such as 'The English Woman's Domestic Magazine' gave advice on rules and regulations of dress, while providing numerous fashion plates illustrating the latest styles. These magazines gave guidance to readers on the whole subject of mourning etiquette and the businesses in the crepe trade thrived. This industry dedicated to death helped those in the crepe business to thrive as it did also for the dyers who made most of their income in dying clothes black for mourning. Where in the past women would have hung up their mourning clothes in their wardrobes in readiness for the next time, now they would not do so for they were persuaded it was unlucky to keep crepe in a household when not in mourning. This clever ploy therefore encouraged those who could afford it to buy the latest expensive dresses, which then distinguished them from those less able to pay, thus reinforcing their superior station in society.

However, Chrissie and her mother had not fallen for any sales pitch and had reused their outfits already bought for Uncle Archie's funeral from 25 George Street, Edinburgh, where gowns, cloaks, handbags, parasols, bonnets, square shawls and widows caps and gloves were sold. At that time, they had also acquired mourning black-bordered handkerchiefs from the Gillies Brothers emporium which was to be found further along the same street.

Chrissie was relieved that society expected a daughter to be in mourning for only one year, unlike her poor mother who would have to do so for two. After a year of being dressed in complete mourning, a widow could then wear a gown of dullish black silk fabric with black embroidery, jet trimmings, black ribbons or lace. Then, after the two years had passed, it would be acceptable for her to dress in soft mauves, lilacs and slate greys, but Chrissie suspected that, like many a widow, Betsy would never come out of black again.

Now that her own year of wearing mourning dress was nearly drawing to a close, she had chosen to wear a gown of heavy bombazine fringed with black on the shoulder in contrast to the white lace collar and cuffs. A string of jet black beads hung round her neck and a pair of long gold earrings dangled from her ears. For this photographic session, and almost in defiance of society's expectations, she wore a tall fetching Spanish-like tortoiseshell comb in her hair, bought for her by Allan on their honeymoon.

At last, the session came to an end, after which Jessie was helped into a warm hat and coat before being bundled into her light wicker perambulator. Chrissie then donned her cloak and hat, shook hands and thanked Mr Henderson, before making her way with her cousin and child to the High Street and to the shops.

First, they visited Andrew Brown's establishment to examine dresses, vests, drawers and hosiery, and then continued along the street to J & T Whittlet, where they could not resist the tempting smell of coffee wafting from within. This was followed by a visit to their favourite Embroidery Warehouse to examine the new and fashionable patterns, where they both made a purchase and bought some baby linen.

No sooner had they left that shop at number 87 than they wandered further down the street until they reached number 93, John Taylor's New Hat Shop. There they discovered, not just an inviting array of hats in satin, felt, straw and tweed, but also an assortment of scarves, umbrellas, bags and leather cases. The emporium even offered trimmings for mourning bonnets, but Chrissie was no longer in need of such a service.

Finally, they stopped at Peter Marshall's baker shop in Kinnoull Street and purchased an assortment of biscuits for Aunt Jessie to whom they were about to pay a visit. They knew how fond she was of a tasty biscuit to accompany a cup of tea.

When they arrived at Bellwood, their aunt was there to greet them. She was particularly taken with Jessie, who had been named after her. Their Uncle John and Aunt Mary were there too, having come over from St Albans Cottage where they lived. He and Aunt Jessie were still running the nursery and making a great success of it by all accounts.

The visitors were ushered into the parlour for tea was about to be served. While Aunt Jessie fussed over the little girl, Chrissie relaxed in the comfort of this room she knew so well with its graceful chairs and sofas, its china cabinet in one corner and piano on the other. The familiar little tables with their variety of ornaments, albums, inlaid boxes and miniatures were still there, as was the mantelshelf with its valance, black marble clock in the centre and 'wally dugs' at either end.

Chrissie took careful note of all this, as she wished to create the same calm and tasteful ambiance in her own parlour at Craig-bank. Already, she had replicated Bellwood's dining room with its large mahogany table and classic Regency chairs, as well as the ornamental mirrors hanging on either side. Already she had invested in a similar large dark green and red Turkish carpet for Craigbank, as well as a buffet and side tables to display the silverware, crystal and china dishes. Both mansions appeared to have a room for every purpose and occupation – bedrooms, dining room, parlour, smoking room, billiard room, nursery (although Bellwood had little need of one) and of course quarters below stairs for the servants.

However, Chrissie's favourite room in Bellwood would always be the library with its heavy dark furniture upholstered in sombre velvet and leather. She was particularly drawn to the book-lined walls with their copies of Walter Scott's Waverley collection, Shakespeare's plays, and its assortment of Bronte, Austin and Gaskell novels alongside a large collection of non-fiction by Goldsmith, Pope and Dryden. Collections of poetry by Byron, Wordsworth and Shelley were also to be found, the pride of place going of course to the work of the Queen's favourite poet, Alfred Lord Tennyson. Chrissie remembered having to read quite a number of these books to her great uncle when he was alive. She felt she could spend a whole lifetime in that one room and vowed to own a similar library at Craigbank.

Soon, while partaking of afternoon tea, all the latest news was shared. Chrissie then chose a moment to announce her own piece of news. She was expecting another child in October. The assembled company were delighted to hear the glad news and all agreed it would be marvellous if it were a boy.

After much animated talk on the subject of babies and children, it was time for Chrissie, Alice and Jessie to leave. They had another visit to make before going to Alice's home at Knowehead. And so, after bidding farewell to everyone, they made their way to the nearby Kinnoull Graveyard for Chrissie wanted to visit the grave of her great Uncle Archie. Once there, she took a few minutes to stand by the grave remembering, not only the grand old man, but also all those in the family who had died and were now buried there too. William Dickson, who had endowed the nursery to her uncle, had been laid to rest there in 1837. Both men had been bachelors and so there were no graves for their wives or children although there was one other Dickson grave – one of William's sisters who had passed away back in 1840.

By now, the three-year-old Jessie was asleep in her pram, giving the two women peace to cross the path and visit another family grave, that of their uncle, the Reverend James Anderson. He had retired to Perth after a lifetime of work in Norham and had died nine years before, but not before conducting the funeral service of Chrissie's other cousin, Christina Leech, who had died of cholera in 1866. She too lay there beside the others.

Meanwhile, Alice was standing further down the path in front of her mother's grave. She had also died when young, leaving her husband, James, to bring up Alice and her brothers at Knowehead. Over the years the aunts had taken it in turn to look after the children and run the home at Knowehead. None, however, had managed to replace the children's real mother.

Then, on moving down the path, Chrissie noticed another family plot nearby. There lay Mr George Gray, her uncle's neighbour, who had recently been interred there alongside many of his 15 children. Mrs Gray, however, despite giving birth to so many, had survived the ordeals and was still alive. The sight of Mr Gray's grave made Chrissie smile, for she remembered how he and Uncle Archie, both crusty old men of over eighty, had gone to the High Court to dispute a piece of land no bigger than eight square yards and which was of no value to either. Mr Gray had purchased a field next to Uncle Archie's, round which there had been a fence, until Mr Gray had it cut down to allow access for his carts to cross a small part of land belonging to Bellwood. For doing so, Uncle Archie had taken him to court and had won his case. However, Chrissie had been told, despite this, the men had remained firm friends until they died and now there they lay near to one another for the rest of eternity.

Many years before, Mr Gray's son-in-law, John Everett

Millais, had produced a painting which had depicted two nuns in a graveyard, one holding a rosary and the other digging a grave. However, Chrissie had been told that the artist had actually painted Mr Gray's garden to represent the graveyard, as he had worked outside to do so, but had added the gravestones on discovering the actual Kinnoull graveyard. The painting had later become famous and was now hanging in a London gallery. What was it called again? Chrissie thought for a moment. She had seen copies of the painting but never the original. She would only have been a child when it had been created, but she could easily visualise it with its October sunset and falling leaves. She had been told the shortened daylight hours had related to the theme of mortality and the cycle of nature. Then she remembered its title. 'The Vale of Rest'. How appropriate.

Soon it was time for them to go to Knowehead House where Alice's father and brothers would be waiting to greet them. Chrissie shivered in the cold and drew her mantle closer. Meanwhile, Jessie slept on in her perambulator, warm beneath the blankets and tired after an exhausting day.

Chapter 2

1886: An Exhibition

As they approached the city's Meadows parkland, Chrissie and Allan could hear the music from the bandstand. The familiar world of Edinburgh had taken on a magic never seen before for, not only was the music of Rossini's overture to 'William Tell' filling the air with its rousing notes, but the whole theatrical scene could be viewed for miles. The trees were hung with hundreds of coloured lamps, coloured fires, port lights and Chinese lanterns. The electric power, according to all the newspapers, was equivalent to a quarter of a million candles and produced the most brilliant and wonderful display ever seen in the country.

Chrissie was particularly excited at there being such a celebration in Scotland, as her mother and father had often spoken of their own visit to the Great Exhibition in London almost a quarter of a century earlier. Now on that balmy August evening of 1886, the Edinburgh International Exhibition of Industry, Science and Art was taking place in seven acres of the Meadows, right in the heart of Edinburgh and only half a mile away from the Castle.

During the day, Chrissie and Allan had, with his brother James and his wife Margaret already visited the Exhibition with their children. They had already marvelled at the huge edifice with its 26-foot-high unicorn and masonic pillars at the entrance, leading into an impressive main pavilion with its high-domed roof decorated with the signs of the zodiac at the front of the building. They had already visited the numerous corridor galleries leading from the main hall, each one filled with the wonders of the age. The newspapers had stated there were over 20,000 exhibits from around the world. Not only that, it was a showcase for the very latest scientific, cultural and social advances of mankind, aimed at providing a space to educate visitors with an array of international curiosities and enlightening objects. Italian furniture was there together with violins from Prague, Turkish embroidery, illustrations of mining, pottery, sugar refining, sea industries, paper making and printing. Modes of transport such as railways, tram-ways and others were all on display, together with a large-scale reconstruction of a typical 17th century Edinburgh street, with the legendary buildings which had long been demolished. The painstaking attention to detail and accurate imitation of the old gateway into the city, the Netherbow Port and Black Turn-pike, had been particularly impressive. The huge construction of the whalebone arch from Shetland also appealed, but, for the Waughs, the favourite item came from their part of Scotland. It was the iron gate of the Carron Works made at the Grahamston Foundry.

Now it was evening and Chrissie and Allan had returned by themselves. Allan's brother and family had returned home and their own children were back in Rutland Street with Chrissie's relations, the Peddies. They had walked amongst the crowd, up Lothian Road to Tollcross, where before them lay the statues and gardens, the fountains and lakes, all depicted in different-coloured lights.

While enjoying the magnificent spectacle, they listened to the military band now playing on the illuminated bandstand, while above, a giant hot air balloon ascended into the warm summer air and lit-up the night sky. Chrissie closed her eyes.

While she heard the magnificent music, the laughter and chatter of the crowd, she could also smell the food offered at the various booths as well as the scent of rich perfumes all mingling in the warm evening breeze. It was good to be alive and to be part of such a spectacular event. She could relax knowing the children were being safely looked after by her mother's cousin, Clara, and her husband. All was well with the world.

Clara's husband, Dr Alexander Peddie, had been elected President of the Royal College of Physicians a few years before, and even now at nearly 70 was still deeply involved in his work. Chrissie always found the doctor and Clara to be such jovial and welcoming hosts, despite belonging more to her mother's generation. Betsy was also staying the night, for she and her husband had always been good friends of the Peddies. The two men had always got on well, Uncle Alexander having been medical adviser to the United Presbyterian Church, while both had been staunch members of the Liberal party.

Betsy, Chrissie guessed, would no doubt, at that very moment, be catching up on all the family news. Clara, being the daughter of the second Dr Anderson in Selkirk, Betsy's uncle, would talk of her brothers and their families, including her brother, Henry Scott. He, like Allan Waugh, was a staunch Conservative and had four times been chosen to be Provost of the Burgh. Now, however, he had retired and, on doing so, had been presented by Lord Napier with a portrait of himself painted by the renowned painter, George Reid. Regardless of his seventy-five years, he was still engaged in his favourite sport of fox-hunting and still could be seen galloping across the countryside. But, despite his success, he too had had to deal with illness and death, their infant son and only 16-year-old daughter having died and now sadly his wife, Margaret, was ailing.

The Peddies' own children were now adults, one son Alick, a doctor, being in Iowa while the other, Henry, also of the medical profession, was living in Edinburgh in Palmerston Place with his wife and children. Clara and Mary, the Peddie's two daughters, had become nurses and were living away from home leaving the other two daughters, Margaret, and the artistic Barbara, still at home with their parents. The Peddies too had lost sons, one in infancy while the other, the 19-year old medical student, Thomas, had suddenly died of meningitis.

Allan and Chrissie knew the heartache of losing children, having not only lost their first-born, Elizabeth, but also, in 1883, their three-year-old Andrew who had died of bronchitis. At the beginning of his illness they had believed he was simply suffering from a summer cold but then it had developed into a cough, his breathing getting rapid and wheezy. Soon he had refused food and drink and rapidly became tired, pale and sweaty. In desperation, Chrissie had turned to Mrs Frederick Pedley's book, 'Infant Nursing and the Management of Young Children' for guidance, but to no avail. She then tried administering Dr Seth Arnold's Cough Killer, Mrs Winslow's Soothing Syrup and Crosby's Balsamic Cough Elixir, but none of them worked. She had even rubbed Holloways Ointment over the little boy's throat as was instructed with no result. Joy's cigarettes promised to afford immediate relief in cases of asthma, wheezy coughs and hay fever but she felt she could not ask a child to smoke, no matter how much the advertisement promised a cure. Finally, she had turned to Dr Peddie for help, but in the end the little boy had died.

Thankfully, she and Allan had already been blessed with the birth of another son, Allan, born in 1879, a bright, healthy and loving boy now hopefully sleeping safely in bed in 11 Rutland Street with his five sisters, Jessie now 11, Alice 9, Minnie 8, Mary 3 and Chrissie 1.

Allan had been named after his grandfather, Jessie after Chrissie's aunt in Perth, Alice after Chrissie's cousin there, Minnie (Marion) after Allan's mother, and Chrissie of course after herself. Unlike these children, who had been strictly named after the various members of the family, Allan had insisted on their other daughter Mary being called after her godmother, a Mrs Mary Turpie Gray, who had been a firm friend of Chrissie's parents, as well as a strong supporter of Avonbridge Church. The Grays had lived both in Edinburgh and the nearby parish of Torphichen but, when Mr Gray died leaving Mrs Gray wealthy but without any children, Allan thought it would be a kind gesture to call the child after her.

While walking through the Exhibition that evening, Chrissie began to ponder on what topics of conversation, other than family, would be discussed in the Peddie household that evening. Perhaps it would be the invention of the motor-wagon by a German called Karl Benz, or the production of the motorcycle or, perhaps on a sadder note, the sinking of the 'Daphne' in Glasgow which left 120 dead. On the other hand, on a brighter note, they might be talking about the Queen's golden jubilee which was to take place the following year. There would be more joyous celebrations in Edinburgh. Then Chrissie remembered it would also be the Peddies' golden wedding anniversary, a further reason for jubilation.

For Chrissie, life overall was good, although one thing always cast a shadow on the proceedings and that was her mother's ever-present distrust of Allan. Despite having been welcomed and allowed to stay permanently at Craigbank, ever since Chrissie's father had died, Betsy had harboured this animosity. Chrissie herself had tried to ignore her mother's attitude to her husband, but she did find Allan not only a hard taskmaster with very high expectations but a husband who showed little affection for herself or the children, other than for their beloved son, Allan. She tried to excuse his behaviour by concluding that he had high expectations of himself which had made him the successful businessman he was. He had come from a lowly background living in Linn Mill Cottage in the village of Torphichen, and helped his father look after his four siblings, Grace, Martha, James and John, at the tender age of 20 when his mother had died. At the same time, he had worked hard and had managed to build up a successful seed merchant's business in Avonbridge, before going on to owning two mills and three quarries, as well as managing to afford to build their lovely Craigbank House. Chrissie therefore felt guilty for having any disloyal thoughts and yet she knew he was a risk-taker, having borrowed £1500 from her mother, as well as other amounts from other members of the family. But then again her mother could afford to lend him the money for she had been left quite comfortably well off what with the legacies from both her Uncle Archie and Uncle James together with the sum for the sale of her husband's farm at Lilliesleaf not to mention the widow's pension from the Church of Scotland. Chrissie reckoned her mother should have been willing to help Allan in his enterprises, especially as he had been good enough to have her to stay at Craigbank.

Despite his lack of affection, Chrissie was always grateful to Allan for the unexpected but very acceptable gifts he would bestow on her from time to time, such as the one planned for the next evening. As they were to be staying for several days with the Peddie family, he had promised to take her to the newly-built Lyceum Theatre. They had missed attending the opening performance three years before when they were to have seen Mr Henry Irving and Miss Ellen Terry in 'Much Ado About Nothing'. But this had taken place only four days before little James had died. However, the handsome theatre with its electric light and spacious mosaic tiled vestibule, not to mention its 2,500 seats – albeit some on wooden benches in the balcony – was still there to be enjoyed. It was said that Mr Irving had donated £1,000 of his own money to the theatre for he always referred to Edinburgh as the 'the city of poetry'. As a mark of his generosity, there now stood two colossal busts of both himself and Miss Terry in the foyer. Chrissie was excited at the thought of seeing this splendid theatre at last, even though it was to attend a Doyle Carte opera and not a Shakespearean play.

She once again inhaled the magic of the night and smiled, for this city she had always loved with its glamour, international appeal and sophisticated society. It was the life of the West End in which the Peddies and the Biltons had come to make their homes that she so envied, for life back in Avonbridge, for all the riches of Craigbank, did not compare. Avonbridge was not Edinburgh. But for the moment Chrissie would enjoy this special evening in the Meadows and bask in the wonders of Edinburgh's International Exhibition.

Chapter 3

1894: A Lesson

17 Danube Street
Thursday

My dear Crissy,

Just a line to say your basin stand has not been sent off. They had to bring it down to the shop, as all the ware which was in it had to be packed. There are a couple of basins and water bottles, chambers and the other items, also a crystal carafe so it is not a clever bargain. There is also a basin splash for the back of the washstand to save the walls. You must return the box that they are in, and I will then settle with the cabinetmaker; send a card to the man when you return them.

When I was at Mrs Little's today I spoke to him about your not being able to keep the fire in all night. He said you must close all the flues, and then it will keep. He said you were real nice folk. I am glad the girls like their rooms. It must be very nice for them. I will be glad to see them when they return to school. Aunty goes off next Tuesday to London. I think the change will do her good. She has not been at all well, yesterday and today. Other folks will be back the beginning of next week.

With much love to you all, in which Aunty joins, and bids me
thank Minnie for her letter.

Your affec. Aunt

Christina Bilton

Chrissie put down the letter and sighed. Why did this aunt
of hers who had written always misspell her name? She had also
been baptised with the same name as herself and her own little
daughter, who at that very moment was painfully scraping her
bow across the violin strings for she was already planning to be a
concert violinist. Chrissie reckoned she would need many years
of hard practice to fulfil such a dream for the sharp penetrating
notes were doing nothing for Chrissie's headache.

She had just returned to the house from a gruelling day's
work at the Avonbridge soup kitchen. The coal miners had been
out on strike since the previous June and now, on that hot August
day, they were still holding out. Chrissie had heard that of the
60,000 miners in Scotland, only 5,000 were currently working.
They were fighting for pay equal with that of the English miners
but it was already beginning to be apparent that many of the coal
seams were running short of coal, thus reducing the need for so
many men For many months now, the average number of days
a miner could be working was four in a fortnight. Slamannan
village, lying in the heart of a thickly-populated mining community, was particularly suffering from the effects of the strike and
nearly a 1,000 children from the various Southern Braes villages
were seen to be queuing daily for sustenance at the soup kitchens
set up by bands of ladies, one of which Chrissie was a member.
Each day, she was made aware of the plight of these hundreds
of men and women, as she made her way to work at the soup
kitchens, while the unemployed scoured through the large
rubbish bins to collect refuse.

While the coal miners suffered greatly, so did employees in
other industries such as the workers in the quarries, mills and
railways. They too were out of work as there was no coal with

which to fuel their engines. Coal was needed everywhere and the lack of it caused owners on the railways and other businesses to turn to England to buy it at an increased rate. While most of the public supported the miners in their struggle, people were already beginning to feel the pinch at both ends: giving to charity while paying higher prices for goods.

While Avonbridge was less of a mining village and showed fewer signs of distress than Slamannan, many of the inhabitants there were complaining about the depressing effect the strike was having on their trades. Allan also complained for he saw the effect it was having on his mill, quarry and the lives of his employees.

But all thoughts of these sorry scenes were quickly dismissed as Chrissie's three vivacious young daughters appeared in the doorway. Jessie, now already nearly 20, Alice 18 and Minnie 16 had all returned from working in the Avonbridge soup kitchen. However, something seemed to be causing them much hilarity and so Alice quickly explained to her mother what was amusing them so much.

"Why, Mama, on the way home we saw the funniest of parades. About a dozen miners were passing through the village headed by a piper. They were dressed in white and wearing black gloves or vice versa."

"Yes, and on their heads they wore tall black hats," interrupted Minnie.

"And at the end of the parade were two burly lads walking along arm in arm with an umbrella full of rents, held high up above their heads," added Jessie. "They were 'guisers' I think."

"Who were they? What were they trying to do?" Chrissie asked.

"Oh, it was obviously a protest march for they held up a banner with 'Victory to the Slamannan Miners' written on it," explained Jessie. "Oh Mama, you should have seen it. It was such fun and so amusing."

"Girls, have you no pity for these men? They are out of

work. Their families are starving. While you come home to this comfortable house with lighting and heating and a good meal on the table every night, these people go home to cold damp houses with no food to eat. Think of that. You have no right to laugh at them."

"Yes, we know, Mama, but do you not think they've got themselves partly to blame? Some of the farmers say that, if they had been more frugal and less extravagant while they were earning, they would not be in such straights now," replied Alice.

"And some people at my school say they deserve to suffer because they are slothful, drunken and feckless," added Minnie.

"Enough of this talk. I will not have it! Do you not understand why they have come out on strike? Would you like to be in a family of seven with your father being able to work only four days a fortnight for which he gets paid less than a shilling? I am ashamed of the three of you, I really am."

"But, Mama, you've seen how some of these miners are destroying fences here in Avonbridge to use for their fires. Fences have been rooted up and carried off. It shouldn't be allowed, Mama. That's vandalism." Minnie put her foot down and her nose up in defiance.

"Don't you be such a smart little miss, Minnie. Go to your rooms at once, all of you. Take off your cloaks and be thankful that you have a place to sleep in and decent clothes to wear. Have you learned nothing of the hardships people are suffering? Have you no understanding of their predicament?"

"Mama, don't be hard on us," Jessie came and sat beside her mother. "Of course we are aware of the misery and poverty all around and we are trying our best to help, but what can we really do? Why does it have to be this way?"

Minnie then came and sat down on the other side of Chrissie, resting her head on her mother's shoulder. "Why can't we all live happily in comfortable houses? Why can't we all eat good food and wear the latest fashions? I would hate to be poor!"

"My dears, there has always been destitution and misery. Some people believe that poor people are being punished because of the way they live, their lack of morality, their drinking and their idleness. Perhaps this is so, but your grandfather did not follow that line of thought, though many of his parishioners did. He always believed that if greater regard were shown to the Bible and its teachings, people would be in a better place. He believed it was his duty therefore not only to help them improve their living conditions, but above all lead them to listen to the word of the Almighty, as He would surely guide them through their troubles. I agree with him. Now run along and get ready for dinner. Could you also ask your little sister to stop making that infernal din? On second thoughts don't say that as she is trying so hard to learn to play the violin. Instead, ask Nanny to bring Georgina down to say goodnight."

"Yes, Mama." With a kiss from all three girls they made their way out of the parlour and up the stairs to their bedrooms.

Chrissie sat deep in thought for a minute. She glanced around the room with its thick red carpet, flock papered walls, heavily framed pictures and large mirror reflecting the many items of fine furniture, silver, crystal and many ornaments. Then she looked up at the grand chandeliers twinkling in the light of the flickering fire burning in the grate, before standing up and making her way to one of the thickly velvet framed windows. There, she looked out on the peace of the countryside in front of her. No hovel for her and her family. Instead, Craigbank House had its warm and generously furnished public rooms, bedrooms (nine in all), its library, not to mention its tennis court, kitchen garden, coach house and three stables, as well as the gardener and coachman's houses. She pondered on how lucky and how privileged the family were.

Her favourite room would always be the nursery with its white distempered walls, warm fire with its fireguard in front and the wipeable oilcloth-covered table, where each of her children had learned their lessons as they had grown up. But the large toy cupboard in the corner of the room had given the greatest delight, for out of it had come dolls, toy soldiers, balls and hoops, paper and paint, brushes and games and all the magic of childhood. In that room, her children's dreams had come alive. It had been a place of princesses and princes, witches and fairies, a place where, through a child's imagination, everything had been possible.

As mistress of the house, she had of course the help of a maid, a nurse for the little children, and a governess for the older ones. As for tending to the garden, Jock had been with them since they were married, and James was always there to look after the horses and to be available to drive the coach when necessary. And if there was any illness in the house, the Waughs could afford to send for the local doctor. These pleasures and services Chrissie knew were beyond most in the community, and she thanked God for his bounty. Yet, as the years went on, she became more and more aware that such wealth did not automatically bring happiness.

She turned back to her aunt's letter still in her hand, folded it and then crossed the room to the rosewood desk, where she filed it away with the intention of replying to it the following day. In doing so, her eye fell upon a little gold and black ring which had once belonged to her mother and was now hers. It was a mourning one and still contained a strand of her father's hair. Her parents had truly loved one another but now both were dead, for her dear mother, Betsy, had passed away the previous year at the age of 80. Dementia had finally taken the old lady's mind but, before it had taken hold, Chrissie would never forget her mother's strength, wisdom and support, particularly during hard times. She had been nearby when all her children had been born and had also been there to comfort her when three of those children, Elizabeth, Andrew and Mary, had died.

Mary. How could Chrissie forget that little six-year-old child with her golden ringlets who had succumbed to her fate so quickly? One day she had been running around, skipping and laughing, but by the next had stopped eating and sleeping, later to be followed by that awful vomiting, and screaming and these frightful seizures. Later they were to learn she had suffered a brain tumour which had developed into hydrocephalus. Nothing could be done for the poor little soul and after six days she had passed away. Mary was buried in Bathgate graveyard under the obelisk which marked Chrissie's father's grave, alongside her sister, Elizabeth, and her brother, Andrew.

Through these times of tragedy, Betsy had always been there to comfort and to help bring up the rest of the children, Jessie, Alice, Minnie, Allan and Chrissie and, just a year before her death, she had been able to welcome another little granddaughter into the fold. The baby, called Georgina, was named after Betsy's father, George Anderson.

Chrissie looked down at the ring and remembered the strong and loving bond between her parents. They had dedicated their lives to the service of God and for very little material reward. A third of United Presbyterian Church ministers at the time her father retired were paid no more than £200 a year.

While putting away the letter and the ring, Chrissie came upon an old piece of yellowing paper and discovered the fading writing of words of a poem she had written so long ago.

'Every young fellow that's hearty and free
Likes well on an evening his sweetheart to see
Like home to the weary, when evening is nigh
Ever spontaneous his thoughts to her fly
Nor he e'er forgets, till asleep he doth lie.
But never had man such a modest fair queen
Round her my arms – I'm as happy as a king
Oh, who could her love on her charms e'er withstand?
Confess it I must she's my heart on demand
Knows't then my darling and give me thy hand
Chrissie Dodds
October 22nd/67'

It was an acrostic love poem spelling out the name ELLEN BROCK, but who she was and why Chrissie had written such a poem was long forgotten. It was dated 1867, when she had been a carefree girl of 19. Now, she was an obedient 45-year-old wife, a mother of six, and mistress of a large house, who had put away such thoughts as romantic love long ago.

She had learned to be a capable wife who could make frocks, sew samplers and work a sewing machine as well as arrange dinner parties, as was expected, always following the correct protocol. Invitations would be sent out at least a fortnight before the event to about 12 people, as that was thought to be a convenient number of guests to entertain. Then, on the evening of the dinner, she would offer sherry or some soft drink to the guests who would be gathered in the drawing room, before going through to the dining room half an hour later. There, the damask-covered table would be laden with silver monogrammed cutlery, crystal glasses and china plates all lit by the candles in their silver candlesticks, each guest of course being served with a napkin and a finger bowl. She would always make sure that soup or fish would be served first as an entree, followed by roast beef, mutton, chicken, turkey or game accompanied by vegetables. Desserts, such as fresh and preserved fruit, ices and sweetmeats, would then follow. After the meal was over and after the men had been left alone to enjoy their port and cigars, she would arrange for her daughters, as they grew up, to play the piano or sing songs.

She had also learned to be a responsible mother by teaching her children how to behave at table while remembering the advice, "Many little vulgar habits and faults of speech and manners are avoided by this companionship." She had made herself familiar with 'The Economical Housewife' by Mrs Beeton and had followed that lady's advice on bringing up children, such as refusing to feed them except at stated hours, teaching them the benefits of 'order and punctuality', and ignoring the crying of babies in order to teach them 'self-reliance'. Rather than beatings, Mrs Beeton recommended that children should be trained and disciplined both to promote their own well-being and that of the family unit.

While she tried hard to adhere to Mrs Beeton's advice, she found it difficult, however, for her husband had different ideas. Allan believed in the more fundamental verses of Christianity which stated that to spare the rod was not simply to spoil the child in practical matters, but it also spoiled the soul. Any disobedience subverted the notion of order. Though disobedience was of itself subversive, it was the idea of rebellion that needed to be punished. Discipline could not begin too early. His normal mode of punishment was to lock the children in a dark cupboard, although more often he believed these offices properly belonged to the nurse; that she should have the trouble of the children, their noise and their romping. In short, the nurse should know her place and the children theirs. However, Allan also believed parents should never fail to gather their children round them daily for stated periods, when he would try to instil in them a sense of their Christian and moral duties and how best to fulfil life's obligations.

He had also insisted on Chrissie giving the girls two books to read, one being 'Women of Worth' and the other, 'I Will be a Lady – A Book for Girls', while, for his one son, Allan, who by now was attending school in Edinburgh, he had suggested 'Get Money: A Book for Boys'. All these books were written by Louise Tulhill. He also approved of 'Young Folks: A Boys' and Girls' Paper of Instruction and Entertaining Literature' in which, much to her son's delight, Robert Louis Stevenson's 'Black Arrow' appeared. Meanwhile, Chrissie made sure the girls had been introduced to Lewis Carroll's 'Alice in Wonderland' and Hans Christian Andersen's 'Fairy Tales', books she herself had enjoyed while growing up.

Perhaps like many fathers, Allan had little real interest in his daughters. To him, the only ones who mattered were the sons and, as Andrew had died in infancy, his only son was now Allan in whom he took great pride. The lad was now 15 and attending George Watsons College in Edinburgh, where he was a boarder. He would, of course, be expected to join the family business, although he always seemed to have been more interested in becoming a doctor. However, all that was in the future and meanwhile Allan was performing well at school. As for his five daughters, their father had little interest in them and hoped they would in time be married off to suitable husbands.

Sometimes Chrissie found it hard to comply with the idea that Allan was not only the head of the family but that also he had derived his authority from God, while she as the wife derived hers from him. This was a belief adopted very much by Allan and had been one that she and Alice had scorned and tittered over when they were growing up. Now, she was expected to go along with it.

Chrissie would also regularly pay 'morning' calls, to friends – although they took place in the afternoon – to make light and cheerful conversation. As she had been carefully taught by her beloved mother, these 'morning' calls were for ceremony, condolence or simply social chat, carefully avoiding any argument or scandal knowing that 'digging the dirt' could only be done with close family members, such as those at Bellwood House. She knew that above all the cardinal sin a wife could commit was to make a complaint or criticism of a husband to anyone.

Allan, meanwhile, was a respected member of the community, 'a man of means', a fervent supporter of the United Presbyterian Church and of the Conservative party, sitting on boards of this and making speeches for that. He was now owner of three businesses for, as well as owning Waugh's grain mill with his younger brother, and a seed dressing plant near Craigbank House for grinding wheat, barley and oats. He had set up the Avonbridge Granite and Whinstone Quarries Company nearly four years ago and from his quarries at Bulliondale, Craigend and Craigbank he sold stone. What was less known perhaps was that the project not only needed an investment but also a loan, which had been provided by both Aunt Jessie in Perth and by Betsy, before she died.

Outwardly, Allan and Chrissie appeared to be a happy couple with a successful business, an impressive house and a band of healthy children. Inwardly, Chrissie knew this to be far from the truth.

She sighed as she put the poem away in a drawer and closed the lid of the desk. Perhaps she had got what she had deserved for had she not, as a young girl, always wanted money and a position in society, in the belief that it automatically would bring happiness? Now here she was trapped in a loveless marriage knowing that Allan did not love her, nor she him, and that the situation had been clear to her for many years. To the world, he seemed a well-respected pillar of the community, but in truth his only interest was his self-importance and his position in society.

This need to impress was truly exemplified at Betsy's funeral for, despite the mutual dislike they had for one another, Allan had arranged the most elaborate occasion, the expenses of which would have course been deducted from the old lady's estate. The first carriage in the procession had contained the clergyman and eight pall bearers, while the next, the hearse, was decorated with gold with black ostrich plumes attached to it and pulled by four black horses, while inside, the coffin was covered with black velvet and surrounded by many flowers. This was followed by the family carriage and then those of other more distant relatives and friends. Chrissie shuddered as she remembered the day. Her mother had lived a frugal but honest life, and this show of wealth would certainly not have impressed her.

Her mother had been the one person in whom Chrissie had confided her innermost thoughts and she in turn did the same. Betsy had never felt comfortable with her son-in-law and the money he had borrowed from her and had promised to pay back was never repaid. She therefore stipulated in her will that the sum borrowed was to be paid back on her death to the sole benefactress who was of course Chrissie. This agreement was made when a woman's property automatically became that of her husband, so Allan had no problem accepting this arrangement. However, with the passing of the Married Woman's Property Act in 1881, that sum would not only go to but stay with Chrissie alone, thus making her a reasonably wealthy woman. Thanks to her mother, Chrissie had been awarded a freedom few women at that time possessed.

Chrissie, on hearing the door open, turned and saw her youngest child standing there beside her nanny. Georgina ran to her mother, a doll tucked under one arm and a wide smile of happiness on her face. This lovely child, with her positive energy and utter joy for life, dissolved any sad thoughts for Chrissie or any vague plans for the future.

Chapter 4

1905: A Decision

In 1900, a new century dawned and in the following year the old queen was dead, having reigned for nearly 64 years. She was replaced by her son, the sleepy-eyed, self-indulgent Bertie. By then the Boer War had been fought and won, leaving Britain as ruler of a quarter of the world's people, and fabulous wealth spilled out of the roaring, belching cities of Great Britain. But, while the rich had always blamed the poor's plight on their idleness and fickleness, a new way of thinking had begun to emerge and people, such as Seebohm Rowntree and others, convinced the Liberal government of the need to deliver welfare and social reform.

At Craigbank House, Allan Waugh continued with his prosperous businesses and was now a Justice of the Peace for Stirlingshire. He continued to be a pillar of the community, particularly through his charity work which often concerned Avonbridge Church, his father-in-law's church. He regularly supplied it with plants and cut flowers for services, as well as for charities such as the Band of Hope. He occupied the Chair at concerts, such as those in aid of the Soldiers and Sailors Farming Association, and also presented the new minister, the Rev. Garvie, with a handsome pulpit gown, cassock and church hymnary on behalf of the ladies of the congregation. The United Presbyterian and Free Churches had merged the previous year. The occasion had been quite a family affair for, according to the article in 'The Falkirk Herald', "Mrs Waugh, in a very graceful manner, placed the gown on the new pastor," while "solos were pleasantly rendered by the young Chrissie Waugh."

Involvement in the various Church events occupied quite a considerable amount of the family's time and in 1895, for example, at a two-day church bazaar in aid of church funds, the Waughs manned a stall, while Minnie played the pianoforte and her father supplied the shrubs and evergreens. Also, during the Boer War, Minnie, although now working as a nurse in Dumfries at the Royal Infirmary, and her sister Chrissie, helped receive socks, tobacco and Christian literature to be "dispatched to the officers commanding the lines of communication at the seat of hostilities in South Africa".

Often, the girls provided part of the entertainment at such events as the Bachelor's Dances or during Church services and soirees, with Alice playing the organ or Minnie and Chrissie singing and performing duets. It was reported in the newspapers that at one such gathering a performance had been "tastefully rendered and listened to with rapt attention". In another report, Minnie's singing of 'We Watched her Breathing' was described as delivered "with fine feeling and sweetness".

While the family was thus busy, their brother, young Allan, was offered a place at Edinburgh University in 1896, and Chrissie rented a flat in 25 Warrender Park Road in Edinburgh for him to live with his oldest sister, Jessie, who would run the house with the help of one servant. Soon both he and Jessie were to be joined first by their younger sister, Chrissie, and then later by the youngest sibling, Georgina, when they became day pupils at George Square, George Watson's College's sister school. There the two youngest sisters took classes in dancing, callisthenics, needlework, dressmaking and cookery. When shorthand and typing were introduced into the school curriculum, they took part in these classes too, for it was believed that girls had to be prepared for the world of work, as well as that of domestic duties, before finally settling down to marriage.

There had been much merriment in the flat during these years, for Allan and his sisters found themselves free from the austere presence of their father and more and more frequently their mother came to stay with them for she too enjoyed the fun and freedom.

Then, in 1904, old Aunt Jessie Turner died in Perth. She had been a very wealthy woman, having run the very profitable business of the Dickson and Turnbull Nurseries with her brother for a number of years. In her will, she left each of her various nephews and nieces quite considerable sums of money but, in the case of her niece, Chrissie, a fund was set up, later to be referred to as the Turner Trust. It bestowed only the interest on the allotted sum to Chrissie with the proviso that, on her death the interest only again would continue to be paid to the unmarried daughters. The lump sum only to be released to any issue of the next generation. As Jessie, Alice and Minnie were past the normal age of marrying, it would mean the children of Chrissie and Georgina – were they to marry – would receive the inheritance.

Chrissie knew well the reason for the complexity of her aunt's will. It had been made in order to preclude Allan, her husband, from obtaining any of the inheritance left to Chrissie, in case she gave him any. He had already borrowed a considerable amount from the old lady and she was making doubly sure that no money of hers was to go near him.

In time, Chrissie's daughter, also called Chrissie, left school and became a secretary in the Sun Alliance Assurance Company in Edinburgh, after having attended Dugdales Secretarial College. Georgina, meantime, the youngest of the family, was still a schoolgirl at George Square. Both were attractive young ladies, brimming with energy and fun.

Meanwhile, regular announcements of their brother Allan's progress were made in the 'Falkirk Herald', submitted of course by his proud father.

In 1897, the newspaper reported:

"We are glad to learn that Allan G. Waugh, son of Mr Allan Waugh, Craigbank, Avonbridge, has completed his first professional examination in medicine at the Edinburgh University."

In 1898:

"We are pleased to note that at the end of the summer session in medicine at Edinburgh University, Mr Allan G. Waugh, Craigbank, Avonbridge, was awarded the Bronze Medal in the physiology class."

And in November 1902:

"At a meeting of managers and directors of the Inverness Northern Infirmary, held last week, the application of candidates for the office of resident doctor was considered, and after a careful examination, a short list of three was chosen. We are pleased to note that one of the three is Dr Allan George Waugh, Craigbank, Avonbridge."

But in August 1905, a very different announcement was made:

"It is with regret that we report the tragic death in Cowdenbeath, Fife, on Tuesday of Dr Allan G. Waugh, only son of Mr Allan Waugh J.P., Craigbank, Avonbridge. The late Dr Waugh was 25 years of age and was locum tenens for Craig, Cowdenbeath. Death took place with painful suddenness, the doctor being found lying dead at the foot of the stairway of Woodside House. The young doctor was well known throughout the district not only for his medical skill, but also for his kind heart and sympathy with his patients. During his short life he endeared himself to all who came in contact with him. At school, and afterwards at college, he showed promising talent which exceeded the ordinary run. In his final medical examinations he gained distinctions and during his University career was awarded medals in various subjects. Death was due to heart disease caused by rheumatic fever contracted in boyhood. The sudden call came as a great shock to his parents and family to whom our deepest sympathy goes out for their sad bereavement."

Similar announcements were to be seen in 'The Scotsman' and in the 'Dundee Daily Telegraph', giving details of the funeral arrangements. The funeral was to be held in Bathgate Cemetery where he would be laid to rest with his grandparents and siblings, Elizabeth, Andrew and Mary. A separate gravestone was later to be fashioned for him in the shape of a cross, and below it the following words were to be inscribed:

'Sacred to the beloved memory of Allan G. Waugh M.B. Ch. B. Edin. who was suddenly called away on 8th August 1905 aged 25 years. Therefore being justified by faith, we have peace with God through our Lord Jesus Christ so He giveth His beloved sleep.'

On the day of the funeral the carriages made their way out of the gates of Craigbank House towards the Bathgate Road and on towards the cemetery. The hearse in front was drawn by horses with black plumes and carried the black velvet-covered coffin decorated with its wreaths of lilies and carnations.

But, as was the custom in Scotland, the six Waugh women, dressed from head to foot in deep mourning, sat motionless at home, the warmth of the summer day sunshine seeming out of place for them. They felt nothing but cold emptiness. Five of them had lost their beloved brother and one her most precious son. All sat, together but apart, each choosing to recollect their own memories of Allan.

Jessie was picturing her little brother, so proud in his George Watsons College uniform, so excited to be going to school, while Alice was remembering how he and she had often played 'doctors and nurses', roles they were to choose in later life. Minnie's memories were of those when she had stood so many times in the cold while proudly watching him play rugby for the school. Chrissie was recollecting her embarrassment on reading all those yearly newspaper reports of her brother's university examination successes submitted by their father. Georgina, meanwhile, could only picture the gentle smiling face of her adored brother, someone who always played with her, no matter how busy he was.

As for Chrissie, she was numb. Now there would no longer be a future for her beloved son; no further professional success, no married life, no children to look forward to, and, above all, no Allan. Her outward demeanour appeared calm and in control, but inside anger was beginning to well up. She and her family had already suffered in so many ways, why again were they to be cheated of happiness? Had she done something wrong? Had she committed a sin to be so punished? Had she not tried to abide by the catechisms she learned as a child and followed the Christian religious teachings throughout her life? She knew the answers to such questions as, "What is the chief end of man?", "What is God?", "What is sin?" She knew the Ten Commandments and had tried to live her life accordingly. Yet, why had God chosen to test her faith throughout her life? Why had He chosen to take two sons and two daughters from her? Early childhood deaths were common but the loss of her 25-year-old son was beyond all understanding. This son of hers had given her so much hope. Why had God taken him from her? She knew from the teaching of the Bible that he was prepared for the next world, but why so soon? She had always been told that that the soul of a believer at death was made perfect in holiness and immediately passed into glory; that the body would be united in Christ and rest in the grave till the resurrection. But that was no comfort to her. She wanted answers.

No longer would there be this precious young son around to talk to and play games with. Instead, she was destined to spend the rest of her life alone with this unloving tyrannical husband of hers, doing his bidding until death claimed her. All the girls had already left Craigbank and, although they would visit from time to time, they would not stay for long. She would be left to see out the rest of her days with this man she so despised. Allan had never really loved her nor shown her much affection. She knew early on in their marriage that she was just an adjunct to his success and that her role in life had been to provide children, run the house and play the part of a dutiful wife. She had played that role throughout the years, but now was she prepared to continue to suffer such an existence?

Her thoughts then dwelt on Craigbank House. It was now solely hers, due to her mother's will. Allan had had to pay back to her the loan he owed her mother which left him unable to maintain the house and so with the money Chrissie received from him, she became the owner. It had indeed brought her much pleasure over the years and she had enjoyed being mistress of it. Certainly, she had to confess, it been one of the main attractions in marrying Allan in the first place. Yes, she had worshipped it but perhaps that had been her sin. The second commandment stated: "Thou shalt not make unto thee any graven image, or any likeness or anything that is in heaven above, or that is in the earth below, or is in the water under the earth. Thou shalt not bow thyself to them, nor serve them for I the Lord God am a jealous God, visiting the iniquity of the fetters upon the children unto the third or fourth generation of them that hate me, and showing mercy unto thousands of them that love me and keep my commandments."

Had Craigbank, which she loved so much and which was now in mourning with its closed curtains, stopped clocks and crepe draped mirrors, become her idol? Was the worshipping of this house her sin? Was this why she had been made to suffer? Slowly, she began to believe that that was so and that she was being punished for her love of Craigbank. In accepting this to be the case and on that momentous day of her only son's funeral, Chrissie made a decision.

She then tried to concentrate on imagining the scene which would at that very moment be taking place. The funeral cortege would have reached the long avenue leading to the graveyard and the coffin would have been carried up the gentle grassy slope to the high granite obelisk standing at the top of the hill, a spot well known to the family, for they had visited it often. Over the years, she had placed flowers for those buried there: her parents, Andrew and Elizabeth Dodds; her three children, Elizabeth, James Andrew and Mary. And now Allan was about to be interred there too and to lie beside the others, but with a separate headstone made in marble to commemorate his life.

Lewis Bilton, her cousin, would be there with his sons from Edinburgh, both his parents now being dead. She knew too the Anderson and Miller families would have come from Perth and that Allan's brothers, John and James would be there. Soon the Reverend Garvie would begin to commit the body of her beloved son to "his final resting place'.

As she pictured the scene, Chrissie vowed that day to abide by her decision.

Chapter 5

1916: A Rebel

Britain had now been at war with Germany for the past two years, but life in Edinburgh had carried on as usual. Chrissie's copy of 'The Scotsman' lay open on the table in front of her as she idly read her way through the advertisements. She noted that Jenners were promoting a quilts and cushions sale, while also reminding customers that their Christmas Bazaar was now on. Chrissie sighed. Another Christmas to organise, but who would be at home this year she wondered?

Alongside that advertisement was another for James Atkinson the jeweller of 80 Princes Street, offering good prices for old silver. Chrissie looked across at her display cabinet and smiled. She would not part with her little collection, no matter how poor she might become. She liked the old snuff boxes and calling card cases which had belonged to past members of the family and was particularly fond of the Dickson tea service left to her by her Aunt Jessie from Perth. Beside it sat a newer teapot upon which these words were engraved:

"Presented to Mrs Allan Waugh as a mark of esteem and respect from the Church Congregation Avonbridge August 1906"

That was the year after Allan had died, the year in which everything changed.

Her husband's business, the Avonbridge Granite and Whetstone Quarries Company, had gone into liquidation partly due to the fact that Slamannan was no longer a thriving mining area, but mainly because he had lost interest in all his businesses. His son's death had a profound effect on him as on all the family. While the grain merchants' business continued to thrive, it did not do so under his ownership as his nephew, James Waugh, had taken it over.

Surprisingly, Allan had agreed with Chrissie that they were better living apart and so he moved to Bulliondale Cottage near Craigbank House. There he continued to work as a Justice of the Peace, still supporting many charity affairs as well as still chairing the many local Conservative Party meetings.

Chrissie meanwhile set up house in Edinburgh, in a flat in Bruntsfield, before moving to Cramond, and then finally settling down in Hillview, a bungalow in suburban Blackhall where she was now living with Jessie, Chrissie and Georgina. Craigbank House lay empty and did so for quite some time, until its original price of £2500 was brought down to £800 to be bought by James Waugh, the same nephew who was also now running the business.

Although their parents were now living apart, all the daughters made regular visits to Avonbridge to see their father, with Minnie and Chrissie even continuing to take part in some of the charity concerts with which he was involved. Minnie, for example, had played the piano and sung 'Ye Bank and Braes o' Bonnie Doon' at one of the Rechabite concerts and at another she had recited the poem 'Papa's Letter'.

Always the Waughs, and the Dodds before them, had supported the various temperance societies of the district, having witnessed at first hand the awful results of 'demon drink' on the poor mining families in the district. The Waughs had also strongly supported the Friendly Societies – the Shepherds, the

Gardeners, the Foresters, the Hibernians and the Rechabites – for these societies had done much to help many a working man avoid dependence on Poor Relief. During her years in Avonbridge, Chrissie had worked hard as a member of the Women's Temperance and Prayer Unions which had fought hard against the establishment of licensed grocers, for they were known to encourage housewives to disguise their secret drinking habits by entering alcohol sales in the women's passbooks as 'aqua' or 'soap'.

But that was all in the past. Now here she was living in Edinburgh with Jessie as housekeeper and Chrissie becoming the breadwinner as a typist with the Sun Alliance Company. Alice was now living in her own home in South Queensferry where she was a district nurse, while Minnie, having worked until a couple of years ago at the Dumfries Royal Infirmary, was now out in France tending to the wounded soldiers there.

Georgina – or Ina as she was now more often called –was also living at home with her mother and sisters and had taken a cookery course at Atholl Crescent College but was now unemployed and doing little other than simply 'gadding about' and having a good time. She regularly attended social functions in town, where many interesting and handsome young men from all over the world were to be found and Ina was taking every chance of meeting these attractive visitors.

Not one of Chrissie's daughters was married.

Chrissie then went on to reflect on her two nursing daughters. When young they had both been influenced by their heroine Florence Nightingale who had been reported as saying, "Why have women passions, intellect, moral activity – these three – and a place in society where not one of these can be exercised? Marriage is but a chance, the only chance offered to women to escape and how eagerly it is embraced."

Until these words had been spoken, the job of nursing had been looked down upon as one only fit for "those who were too old, too weak, too drunken, too dirty, too stupid or too bad to do anything else" as Miss Nightingale had put it. In the past, the intimate body services to be done for the patient were considered to be unseemly or immodest for young unmarried well-bred females. Cleaning and feeding another person, especially if not a family member, were regarded as domestic tasks performed by servants. But, by the time Alice and Minnie had become young ladies, a series of nurses' training schools had begun to produce educated women who were then eagerly accepted by hospital authorities. Medical officers, patients and public opinion in general were now demanding higher levels of nursing skills in the wards. Perhaps her daughters had been influenced by the stories Chrissie might have told them of her cousin, Christina, of whom she had had such high regard, when she had trained to be a nurse but of course had died of cholera when young. Perhaps too they had been influenced by their brother's choice of career and had taken an interest in his medical studies. Whatever it was that led to their choice of career, they had devoted their lives to it.

Minnie had joined the Territorial Force Nursing Service in 1914 and was sent to France where, on that first Christmas of the War, she was proud to be one of the 300 nurses abroad who received a canvas bag laced up with red and white ribbons, Queen Alexandra's colours, containing a photo of the Queen, a Christmas card, notepaper, acid drops, a tin of chocolates, a fur-lined cape, a hood and a muff.

Now, having been made a theatre sister, Minnie was working in 45 Clearing Station, 12 and 72 General Hospitals somewhere in France and, although Chrissie knew these addresses from the various letters she received from her daughter, she had no idea where Minnie was stationed. She did suspect, however, that life was tough for sometimes Minnie had described the conditions in her letters. She outlined how the medical teams had to administer to the sick and wounded under enemy raids and shell fire, how they tried to attend to large numbers of men suffering from gas attacks, and how useless they felt sometimes when they were unable to relieve their agony, there seeming to be no remedy.

Chloroform had even been used to try and relieve the suffering, but it had been to no avail.

Chrissie looked across the room to the table where Minnie's framed photo took pride of place. There she was in her sister's blue-grey uniform with its white linen collar and cuffs and white muslin cap. The detachable grey band on her lower arm, with the top and bottom of it piped in red, denoted that she was a sister, while on her blue-grey shoulder cape with its red facing, the small silver plated 'T' badge worn diagonally at each corner stood for Territorial.

Minnie came home every six months and, although she said little of what she was experiencing to her sisters, she had confided some things to her mother. She described how she was always exhausted, sometimes having been working for 24 hours a day in the operating theatre. Conditions had been extremely dire when she had first gone out to France with sometimes only travelling tables, one steriliser or perhaps only three jugs of sterilising lotions for the instruments with which to carry out operations. To begin with, dressings were not sterilised and empty petrol cans served for the soiled dressings. Eventually, however, conditions had improved and trestles had appeared to be used as stretchers, while quantities of comforts such as sheets, feather pillows, socks, pyjamas and dressing gowns appeared, largely provided for out of donations and private funds from those at home.

While Minnie coped with the many horrific wounds and took part in emergency operations in the middle of battle, she had confided to her mother that her most difficult task was in the writing of letters to the soldiers' families informing them of the death of their loved ones.

When Minnie was home on leave, the house was filled with the smell of cigarettes. She had taken up the habit of smoking to get rid of the 'grey backs'– the lice – which infested the men's clothes when they arrived from the trenches. Chrissie did not approve of the habit but Minnie was forgiven and the packets of 'gaspers' lying about in every room were tolerated.

That day, however, there was no smoke to smell for Minnie was in France and Chrissie was sharply bought back to the present when the chimes of the grandfather clock in the hall struck six. She wondered where her two youngest daughters had got to. Chrissie, her daughter, was not working that day and the two of them had decided to 'do the shops' in Princes Street, Chrissie having to return books to the Boots' Book Lovers Library. She had recently acquired John Buchan's 'The Thirty Nine Steps' which they had all read and now they were waiting to read his new book, 'Greenmantle'. Chrissie also knew that the two of them were sure to make their way to Jenners to inspect all the finery there, as well as taking afternoon tea at the Palm Court Restaurant in Patrick Thomsons on the Bridges where a small orchestra would be playing.

Sometimes they would attend the showing of a film at the Picture House in Princes Street with its mock Grecian pillars and stained glass windows; or go to the large Coliseum in Fountainbridge; or even venture to the Palace, the plushest of the cinemas, with its heavy white Sicilian marble columns, its smoking room and its celebrated Wedgewood Cafe. Quite recently they had all gone there to see that funny little actor, Charlie Chaplin, in 'The Tramp'.

Quite often, they would all attend a play at the Theatre Royal at the top of Broughton Street, or one at the Lyceum in Grindlay Street. They would also all enjoy being together to listen to a concert at the Usher Hall in Lothian Road and had, only two years before, managed to obtain tickets for the opening concert in that splendid building with its Doric columns, sculptures and its vast white and gold auditorium. Afterwards, she remembered reading that 3,000 people had been in the Hall that June evening to hear Beethoven, Mendelssohn, Wagner and Elgar's marvellous 'Imperial March' as the finale. Such an experience would never be forgotten. However, she knew the girls had not planned to go to a play or a concert that afternoon, so where were they?

She could hear Jessie in the scullery preparing the evening meal and Chrissie knew her daughter would not be pleased if her sisters were not there at the proper time. Good old Jessie. Where would they be without this quiet, dependable housekeeper? She had become plain and comfortable and complained little, but she played an important place in their lives.

Suddenly Chrissie heard the sound of the key in the latch, then the opening of the front door, followed by giggles and laughter. Then the door of the living room burst open and there stood Chrissie, cheeks red as if she had been hurrying. But where was her sister? Where was Ina?

"Mama, I've something to tell you, but first you must sit down and take in calmly what I'm about to say."

"I am sitting down. What is it? Why is Georgina not with you? Has she been hurt? Where is she?

"Mama. We did not go to the shops today. Instead, we went to church"

"Church? Well, that's very good but which church?"

"St Mary's Cathedral at the top of Leith Walk."

"That's Catholic. Why did you go there?"

"Because .... You're not going to like this, Mama."

"Oh, for pity's sake tell me and have done with it!"

"Ina was married there this afternoon. I was her bridesmaid."

Chrissie froze for a minute. Surely this wasn't happening. Suddenly she stood up and went across to her daughter.

"Married? In a Catholic Cathedral? Why are you tormenting me with this? This has not happened. Tell me this is not true."

"It is, Mama. Ina is a married woman."

"This is all bluff."

The young Chrissie shook her head.

"Who has she married?"

"You don't know him, Mama. She met him at one of these soirees at the Assembly Rooms. I was with her when she met him and she swore me to secrecy, for she knew you would disapprove."

"Disapprove! Of course I disapprove! What would her grand-father, my father – a good Protestant minister – think of all this? A Catholic in the family!"

"Mama, not all Catholics are bad and he is a very lovely man."

"You don't know what you are talking about. And any chil-dren they have will have to be brought up in that evil faith. What is the name of this so-called husband of hers anyway?"

"Mama, I don't think you'll like this either. His name is Jack Flannery?"

Now Chrissie's hands flew to her head in utter incredulity.

"Flannery! Flannery! But that means he's Irish! She's married a Fenian! Oh, how can I stand this? What did I do to deserve this disgrace?"

During the previous year, the newspapers had been full of the unrest in Ireland, culminating in the Easter Rising in Dublin. The Irish Republicans had tried to end British rule there, for they had wanted to set up an Irish Republic. She had read of the fierce street fighting in the capital city and of the heavy casualties that had been inflicted. She had also read the moving but rebellious poem written by the poet W. B. Yeats, which had been published soon after. But all that had little to do with her until that moment. Had her daughter married one of those rebels?

Chrissie put her head in her hands and rocked to and fro.

"Who is he, this .... this Jack Flannery?"

She spat out his name as if it were a nasty taste in her mouth.

"What does he do? No doubt a soldier."

"Yes, Mama, he is a soldier. He's a second lieutenant in the Lovat Scouts."

To try and make her mother understand that Jack was a good man, Chrissie rambled on.

"Although his family originally came from Cork, he was born in Aden in the Yemen for his father was in the regular army there and fought in the Afghan Wars. Jack was first brought up in Cork and then Inverness. His family are very respectable, Mama.

Please try and be happy for them. Ina is the only one of us sisters who has fallen in love and got married."

Chrissie was not comforted by these details, for hadn't life been fine without any man coming on the scene to disturb their orderly lives? They had managed well without the opposite sex. Now this. And who was this unknown young man anyway?

"How old is he?"

"Well, Ina told a little fib and said she was 22 when we all know she's 26. She did that as he's only 21 this month."

"A baby-snatcher into the bargain! What was she thinking? Where are they now?"

"They're standing out there in the hall. Please, Mama, don't be too hard on them. They so much want your approval."

Then the door opened and there stood Ina, accompanied by a boyish slim, fair-haired young man. He was dressed in khaki jacket, shirt, tie, breeches, puttees and black boots. Chrissie recognised it as the uniform of the Lovat Scouts, having recently read an article on Lord Lovat. All this was confirmed by the famous silver badge with the Fraser of Lovat's crest, a Royal stag with the well-known motto 'Je Suis Prest' (I am Ready), attached to the young visitor's jacket lapel, as well as the regimental brass buttons sporting the same crest and the words 'Lovat Scouts I.Y.' (infantry Yeomanry).

The clear blue eyes of the young man shyly caught hers. They seemed to express abject apology, like a child who had been caught with his hand in the sweetie barrel, and Chrissie could not help but be attracted to him despite his being Catholic and Irish. He seemed still to be a boy, too young to have taken part in any fighting.

Meanwhile Ina was all smiles and giggles, while knowing full well how shocked her mother must be. Undaunted, however, she took her new husband's hand and nestled into his side in quiet defiance. Chrissie had to admit to herself that her pretty young daughter looked blissfully happy in her fetching new outfit of navy three-quarter length coat, blue serge dress with hobble skirt and fetching tall feather trimmed hat. All these items no doubt having been bought 'on the sly' by her older sister, for Ina had little money of her own.

Chrissie moved forward to greet the young couple as in a dream, not quite real. She found herself going through the motions expected of polite society and heard herself congratulating the couple on their marriage, appearing warm but with her heart turned to ice. She shook the young man's hand as manners dictated but, when he spoke, she was pleasantly surprised by his gentle, educated voice.

Meanwhile, Ina kissed her mother in the usual affected manner she had come to adopt when wishing to give the impression of sophistication, and then proceeded to take a cigarette from her handbag, place it in a long cigarette holder, light up and calmly exhale smoke in the same affected style. Then she turned to her young man and defiantly flirted with him in a most provocative and seductive manner, knowing full well how distasteful her mother found such behaviour.

Just then Jessie, who had heard all the laughing and talking coming from next door, emerged from the scullery. She too greeted the news with shock, but immediately congratulated the two with a hug and a kiss. Poor Jessie, in her overall not yet discarded, had never experienced the love and affection of any man and was not likely to do so now. Unlike this affected young sister of hers, she possessed no pretensions, no affected mannerisms, but had always been a true, loving, kind and caring person to everyone she met. Surely, thought her mother, she had deserved more than her present state, but there she stood delighting in her young sister's happiness.

Through the excitement and over a cup of tea, Chrissie wondered how Alice and Minnie would respond to the news when they heard it. She was sure neither would approve. They had lightly dismissed their pretty youngest sister's flighty ways as simply those of impetuous youth, but Ina had done little of worth to alleviate the ills of society; in fact, the world of work in any form did not appeal to her. Edinburgh had offered a world of excitement and glamour and now, with this War on, there were many attractive young men from all over the globe ready to flirt with a pretty young girl and give her a 'good time'. Ina had little need for a life of boring work. Romance was in the air and she couldn't wait to fall in love. Now she had. But would she live happily ever after? Only time would tell.

Above all the celebratory excitement, Chrissie heard her youngest daughter's voice ring out strong, confident and as brittle as ever.

"Because of this damned War we have to do everything so fast. Time is never on our side."

As she spoke, the young bride put her head to one side and glanced coyly at her new husband who innocently smiled back. Feeling he ought to supply a bit about himself, Jack went on to explain how he had joined the Lovat Scouts because his father had been commissioned by Lord Lovat to train recruits in Inverness after he had been in the Indian Army all his life and after fighting in the Afghan Wars. Jack had duly received his commission and had become 2nd Lieutenant before joining his father to fight at Gallipoli the previous year. Now, he was aiming to join the Imperial Camel Corps the following month and was at that present time training in Glasgow, but would soon be in Chelsea for a spell and then Besley before making his way out to the Middle East.

"He's going to ride a camel. Isn't that such fun?" added Ina in deep admiration of her young hero.

After a short while, the young couple had to make a move to leave. They were off to Blair Atholl in Perthshire for their honeymoon. Ina giggled at the mention of such an event and gave Jack a cheeky and knowing look. Almost apologetically, he then explained that after that they would be on their way to Inverness to visit his parents and to see his two sisters, Doreen and Eileen.

"But now we must love you and leave you, Mama. I'll be back in a few days but Jack will unfortunately have to return to Glasgow."

With these few words, everyone stood up and again hugged, kissed and shook hands with the young couple before they exited as fast as they had arrived. This all happened in a fashionable whiff of lavender and jasmine from Ina's 'Aqua di Parma Colonia' perfume.

After all the glamour and excitement had vanished with the banging of the front door, Chrissie and her daughters stood there transfixed. Slowly each then looked at one another before Jessie went back to the scullery to continue making the tea. Chrissie, the daughter, now no longer the bridesmaid, went across to her room to change out of her 'glad rags' while Chrissie, the mother, sat down and stared into the fire burning cheerfully in the fireplace.

After a few quiet moments she looked up and her eye caught the large portrait of the formidable Aunt Jessie Turner hanging above the mantelpiece. What would she have thought of this marriage? Why, she hadn't approved of Chrissie's own choice of husband so long ago. This match would have been beyond her wildness nightmares. An Irish Catholic in the family! She would not have endured such a relationship. But what could she have done? Nothing. She had been dead for over 12 years and time had moved on since the old witch in the portrait had ruled Bellwood. A World War was now raging, and the beliefs and values of the Victorian age were rapidly receding.

And who was Chrissie herself? Nothing but a 68-year-old woman, most of whose life was over. She did not have the right to spoil it for those whose lives were before them. Nevertheless, in the pit of Chrissie's stomach she felt unease. Where would this all end? Why was this youngest daughter of hers so different from the others, and why was she so affected, so spoiled and so headstrong? Why did she delight so much in defying her? Chrissie knew well that Ina had revelled in the fact that her marriage had taken place without her consent and that she, Chrissie, could do nothing about it.

As soon as the questions came to Chrissie, the answer soon

followed. Her youngest daughter had certainly been spoiled but there was more to it than that. At 15, she had lost the person who was most dear to her. She had lost her brother, Allan, who she had always idolised. While they had all mourned Allan's death, it had been Georgina who had suffered most. He had been so protective of his little sister and she had always been so proud of him. After his death, she had refused to return to school and from then on had seemed uncertain of anything. Behind the jarring veneer of sophistication, Chrissie suspected there was an insecure, unconfident and slightly depressed young woman who felt cheated by life.

As for her choice of husband, Chrissie rather liked Jack Flannery and he certainly seemed smitten by her daughter's charms. But then did they really know each other? How would this marriage turn out? Would they live happily ever after? Only time would tell. With all her heart Chrissie wished them well.

But now came the next hurdle, which Chrissie dreaded. She must inform the other family members before they read the announcement in 'The Scotsman'. How would the Peddies and Biltons in Edinburgh, the Andersons and Millers in Perth, the Waughs in Torphichen receive such news? What would Alice and Minnie think? Above all, how would Allan in Avonbridge respond? Chrissie dreaded to think.

In August of the following year, when young men were falling at the Battle of Passchendaele in France and others were revolting in Russia, Chrissie sat in her home in Blackhall, four of her daughters by her side, awaiting news. Ina was about to give birth in one of the bedrooms, but Jack was not with them for he was now down south completing his training.

The small group of women had not long to wait for soon a baby's yell was heard. They all stood up excitedly clapping their hands. Was it a boy or a girl? Very soon the door opened and out came the midwife. Ina had just given birth to a little girl whose name they all knew already. Here was another Christian, called after her grandmother as was the custom.

When she was brought through to the family, swaddled in a warm bundle of blankets, the child was gently placed in her grandmother's arms. Chrissie then silently put up a prayer to God to protect this vulnerable little thing through a long, happy and secure life. Christian Turnbull Flannery, to be known as Kitty, had arrived.

Part 6

Georgina's Story

Chapter 1

1920: A Funeral

Ina found herself alone looking out of the window while marvelling at the silent scene before her. The snow was feathering down from the leaden sky as she knew it would also be doing on the silent mourners on their way to her father's funeral at Bathgate Cemetery. White on black. In contrast, the room in which she was standing, was full of noise and bustle, the female members of her family preparing the meal for the return of their men folk for, as was the custom in Scotland, women did not appear at the graveside.

Ina was back in the house that had once been her home. She was back at Craigbank. Fifteen years had passed since she had looked out from the same window and had watched another family funeral cortege making its way to the cemetery. Then, it had been a warm summer's day in August; this time, it was on a cold and frosty one in December. Then, it had been the funeral of a young man with everything before him; now, it was that of an old man with nothing before him. Both men had been called Allan Waugh. In 1905, the family had buried her brother; now, they were burying her father. At the first funeral, she had been a 15-year-old schoolgirl; now, she was a 30-year-old wife and mother.

Now Craigbank House belonged to her cousin, James Waugh, who had bought the house from her mother as well as taking over the family business. It had been decided that it was the most appropriate place in which to hold the wake.

Her 72-year-old mother stood ramrod straight, displaying the usual stoicism and determination with which she had governed her life. Outwardly, she appeared dignified and assured, but inwardly Ina wondered what exactly was going on in her mind. What did she feel? Did she feel anything? After all, fourteen years had passed since she had left her husband to come and live in Edinburgh with her daughters. Did she regret her decision? Had she ever really loved her husband? Throughout her married life, she had worked tirelessly for the church, always supporting the sick and the poor just as Grandmother Dodds had done before her. She had brought up her children to serve the community and so it was not surprising that her son, Allan, had become a doctor and two of her daughters nurses.

But then, with Ina's brother's death, everything had changed. Her mother, displaying a determination and more than a little cold-heartedness, had left her father to enjoy her independence as a member of the genteel middle classes in Edinburgh, with whom she shared their narrow-minded and judgemental atti-tudes. Ina would never be allowed to forget that her own choice of husband would forever rankle with her mother, and that she would never truly be forgiven for what she had done.

As for her four sisters, not one of them had married. Ina wondered, as she had often done in the past, how much her parents' unhappy marriage had influenced the course of their lives. Perhaps they had chosen to be single, to be masters – or mistresses – of their own fate, perhaps not wanting to be 'angels in the house' or second class citizens.

Jessie was still housekeeper to the family and continued to live a quiet life, always dedicated to providing meals and comfort for her mother and her sisters. Chrissie was the sister to whom Ina would always be closest and who had been so supportive on her wedding day, officiating as bridesmaid. Ina had always firmly believed that Chrissie was the one who should have married, who should have had children, but sadly it was not to be. Now at 35-years-old, she was destined to be the chief wage earner.

Ina's other two sisters had long since left home. Alice was a district nurse living and working in South Queensferry, while Minnie had not long returned from the Front and was about to continue her nursing career back in Scotland, still as a member of the TFNS. Perhaps she had been the one closest to their father, and, when she was awarded the honour of being Mentioned in Despatches, he was particularly happy.

And what of herself? Unlike the other sisters, she did find love and a husband and she did produce a child. But had she found happiness? She was not sure. Jack and she had fallen in love and married so quickly in 1916, but had they really known each other? A few days after the honeymoon, he had left to train to be part of the Imperial Camel Corps and had soon found himself in Palestine fighting the Turks. The few times he did manage to come home on leave had not been successful, the only one to truly welcome him, besides herself, being Chrissie.

The family's suspicions of her 'Fenian' husband were confirmed when he was temporarily court-martialled for being drunk. It happened on the September of the following year while training at Beccles. He was caught drunk on whisky while in charge of a lorry and was convicted for being unfit for duty the next day "by reason of previous indulgence in alcoholic stimulant". For this he was severely reprimanded and punished by losing a year's seniority. The incident only confirmed Ina's mother's suspicions of Jack all along and, although he was quickly reinstated by the Army, the damage had been done. Forever after, the Waugh family had branded him as an Irish drunk.

The scourge of alcohol was playing a large part in the psyche of many people by that time, with an ever-increasing support in the country for campaigns to prohibit strong drink entirely. The Temperance Movement, supported by Christianity,

Chartism, Socialism and the Women's Suffragette Movement, gathered momentum, encouraging many people to make a pledge in church or at temperance meetings to abstain from 'the evil drink'. Certainly, over the years in Slamannan, Ina's family had witnessed its devastating effect on miners' families and the Waughs were always amongst the strongest supporters of the Temperance League in nearby Falkirk in its fight for total abstinence. Her sisters had sung and performed many times at many of the Rechabite concerts given in the area.

Several years before, the Defence of the Realm Act led to stricter controls on public houses. Beer was watered down and with an extra penny tax added to a pint, many publicans lost the interest in selling drink. A 'No Treaty' rule forbade buying rounds of drinks, and there was soon a meeting in London to ban all alcohol consumption, but it was voted down.

A big secret Ina had carefully kept from the rest of the family, including Chrissie, was that during her younger days of socialising and 'being out on the town', she had indulged in enjoying several fine drinks over the years. She vowed, however, that her family would never learn of this, for she knew how much they would disapprove.

On this day of her father's funeral, Ina was alone. Jack, although on his way home, had not yet returned, and their three-year-old daughter, Kitty, was being looked after by a neighbour back in Edinburgh.

The years since her marriage had been hard for Ina, her only real joy being the birth of Kitty. The child was fast growing into a very attractive little girl with her fair hair and blue eyes, just like her father's, and was full of mischief and fun. Even then, Ina sometimes regretted the child's presence, for it tied her down and restricted her social life. How she longed for the day when Jack would return and they and little Kitty could all live together in their own home, away from her family's constant disapproval.

Soon the male mourners began returning from Bathgate and were led by the man of the house, her cousin James. Not far behind him came Lewis Bilton, her mother's cousin and the family lawyer, accompanied by his son, also called Lewis and also a lawyer. Lewis's wife, Hannah, and their daughter, Chrissie, another nurse, came forward to greet them. Other cousins of her mother also began to arrive. George and James Miller from Perth, again both lawyers, joined their sister, Alice Roberts. She had been her mother's bridesmaid and, although she had married at quite a mature age, she was now widowed. Other friends and members of the family began to fill the large drawing room, a room which had been so familiar to Ina in her childhood, but now meant nothing to her.

She also felt alien towards all the people in the room. She regarded them as firm representatives of the middle classes, secure in their beliefs and their ways. Most were wealthy, industrious, law-abiding, church-attending pillars of society. Ina regarded most of them as being smug, self-satisfied and judgemental. Certainly most of them disapproved of her marriage to Jack.

Quietly, she crossed to where her coat was hanging, slipped it on, and made her way outside to a sheltered corner of the garden which had been a favourite spot for her as a child. The old seat under the oak tree was still there, and so she sat down, despite the temperature and the gentle falling snow. No one would miss her. While there, she began to wonder just how much these relations of hers actually knew about Jack. Indeed, how much did she herself know about him? Some facts of course she knew, both from his telling her but by taking the time to read as much as she could in the newspapers, she had a firmer understanding of the War than many other people..

Jack had been born in the Yemen, his father having spent his life as a soldier in the Indian Army fighting in the Afghan Wars. Captain Flannery and his second wife then settled in Inverness with their family. There Jack had attended school.

Two years later, Lord Lovat had taken command of 70 young men who wished to become part of the Highland Mountain

Brigade and he had formed the 1st and 2nd Lovat Scouts. On doing so, he had approached Jack's father to lead a working party of about 20 civilians to prepare a camp at Beaufort Castle for the training of these two regiments and, although Captain Flannery had been planning to retire, he nevertheless agreed to do so.

By the beginning of the War, both regiments, each by then consisting of around 1200 men, had become part of the Territorial Army and by this time Jack, at the age of 18, was given a commission, had become a Second Lieutenant and had joined his father. With other young men, he was billeted in farms near Beaufort during his training, before setting off for the battle station at Huntingdon. Soon after he found himself sailing with the others, including his father, to Alexandria. From there on they headed towards the Greek island of Limnos, whose harbour had become the base for the allied forces for the bloody battlefield of Gallipoli. There they worked for 12 days on night fatigue duties, unloading and carrying ammunition and stores such as drinking water and rations, as well as digging trenches. Captain Flannery was still officiating as Quartermaster and was in charge of supplying the men with tea, bully beef, sugar, biscuits, jam, blankets, waterproof sheets, boots and cigarettes, as well as supplies sent from home such as socks, shirts, handkerchiefs, soap and even eau de cologne.

Jack, like all the others, had found it difficult to sleep during the day because of the heat, the sound of the rifles, and the sight of such large numbers of unburied corpses lying between the lines. Other than tiredness he remained well, unlike many soldiers there who soon began to feel sick after being there for about two days. Most of them suffered from stomach troubles and others from heatstroke, and while they were moving up to the front-line trenches, water had been scarce. It had to be boiled and rationed, and while their enemies were the Turks, their real enemy had been dysentery. However, while there were many casualties from exposure and jaundice, none of the Scouts died, and the only two Lovat Scouts to be taken prisoner throughout the War were taken at Gallipoli. They had been two mess order-lies who, while carrying tea to the front line, had missed their way and walked right into the Turkish trenches.

Jack and his father were there for nearly three months and on the front line, patrolling and sniping in the face of much hardship, before the hopeless stalemate of the campaign had been recognised by the government. Orders were then given for the evacuation of the peninsula, but Jack and his father had continued to fight, along with the Ghurkhas, right on until nearly the end of that year, until the retreat. Despite the appalling storms, floods and snow, a shortage of rations and water unfit to drink, and with their soiled clothing frozen into hard boards on their bodies, the Highland Mountain Brigade became the rearguard at Suvla Bay and successfully provided cover for the final withdrawal. Gallipoli suffered half a million casualties, between the Allies and the Turkish soldiers, and was later to be described as a holocaust, second only to the carnage at the Somme.

But Jack and his father survived, although Captain Flannery was admitted to hospital with malaria first in Malta and then Sicily. However, by the summer of 1916, he had been well enough to rejoin the regiment, by which time the Lovat Scouts had been formed into one infantry battalion and had become part of the Cameron Highlanders. They were re-organised, re-equipped and drilled as infantrymen before leaving for Salonika, where they were to stay for eight months.

As for Jack, he decided to join the Imperial Camel Corps for, having been born in Aden, he wished to be back in the Middle East. Six new companies had been raised from British yeomanry regiments which were to become part of the Imperial Camel Corps. This self-contained, completely independent fighting force had been formed to take over the job of patrolling and maintaining contact with the Senussi in the desert areas to the west of the Nile Valley and north of the Sudan. The first unit, the 1st, 3rd and 4thBattalions, was to be made up of Australian and New Zealand mounted regiments, but the 2nd was to be formed almost entirely of British yeomanry recruits and it was to this regiment that Jack was assigned. It was during this time in his training in Glasgow that he had met and married Ina and very soon after went off to Palestine.

Things had not been going well there for the British, for their defeat and inability to dislodge the Turks from the Dardanelles exposed the Suez Canal to potential attack. Meanwhile the Arabs, viewing the involvement of the Ottoman Empire as an opportunity to revolt and drive the Turks from their land, had seized the chance brought about by the War to harass their enemy. The British had lent support to them through shipments of arms and money, but the revolt had sputtered on and was in danger of collapsing. Then a young Captain TE Lawrence was sent out to bring order and direction to the Arab cause. This introverted and studious young man was to become one of the most colourful military figures of the War, for he and his band of Arab irregulars had attacked Turkish strongholds for two years, severing communications, destroying railways and supporting the British regular army in the drive north to Damascus.

Jack arrived in time to be involved in the capture of Jericho in February 1918 and, by the end of the month, the west bank of the Jordan had been completely cleared of the enemy from Jericho to the Dead Sea. However, the journey to Jericho had not been an easy one and, at the end of marching for 18 hours by the Dead Sea, the soldiers' troubles had only just begun. The terrain had changed and the camels had struggled gamely to find a foothold, but they were not designed nor accustomed to such appalling conditions. It had rained without a break and getting the camels back was deemed impossible, and so the soldiers had had to remove their loads and reluctantly shoot them. The weather becoming worse, the men had slept as they walked, and all the time the Turks had had them in range and continued sniping at them as they journeyed on.

When the British troops did eventually arrive in the Jordan

Valley, General Allenby decided to disband the Camel Corps, as it had been proved that camels were hardly suitable for the sort of country over which any further advance would have been made. However, he gave Lawrence 300 hundred men for operations against and beyond the Hejaz railway, later to be known as the Arab Revolt, the Arabs having agreed to revolt against the Ottomans and fight with the allies, for the promise of Arab independence after the War.

From the 26 British companies, two were chosen to fight with Captain Lawrence and Jack was in one. However, while some soldiers did succeed in reaching their destination and did manage to blow up parts of the railway line, they did not damage the station or the tunnel complex as planned.

At the end of the war, despite the United Kingdom and France having agreed to support Arab independence as a reward for their aid during the revolt against the Ottomans, they did not keep their word. According to the terms of the Treaty of Versailles, Arabia was divided up in ways that were unfavourable to the Arabs with France gaining Syria and Lebanon, and Britain Mesopotamia (later Iraq) and Palestine. And, because of the promise made in the Balfour Declaration, Palestine became the Jewish national home. The possessions of the Ottoman Empire became the Kingdom of Hejaz, which the British then duly gifted to the Al Said family. Much later it was to become Saudi Arabia. The Kingdom of Yemen remained a British protectorate as did Kuwait, Bahrain and Qatar.

Jack had felt most bitter about the way in which the Arabs had been treated and so decided to follow in his father's footsteps and join the Indian Army. He was granted a permanent commission, was attached to the 1/8 Ghurkha Rifles and continued to serve in the Battle for Syria. The months of fighting had then continued but now they had come to an end and Jack was on his way home to Edinburgh, to his wife and daughter.

To Ina, Jack would always be her hero who had fought so bravely for his country but she knew that, to her family and those people gathered that day in Craigbank House, he would always be regarded as 'an Irish drunk'!

With that in mind, Ina stood up and slowly walked back through the snow to the house. Soon she would be free of these awful people ahead of her, and soon her heroic husband would be back home with her.

Chapter 2

August 1923:
A Confrontation

Jack eventually did return to Edinburgh to join his wife and little daughter, but it was not to 'a land fit for heroes', as had been promised by the then Prime Minister, David Lloyd George. Instead it was one in which a seventh of all men were out of work, Jack becoming one of them.

Also, in that same year, the Reverend White, a Church of Scotland minister, was involved in the publication of a report entitled 'The Menace of the Irish Race to our Scottish Nationality'. It accused the Roman Catholic population in Scotland of subverting Presbyterian values and of drunkenness, crime and financial imprudence. It called for the ending of immigration of Irish Catholics to Scotland, and the deportation of any convicted of a criminal offence or living on state benefits. White urged a 'racially pure' Scotland, declaring "Today there is a movement throughout the world towards the rejection of non-native constituents and the crystallization of national life from native elements."

The report of course echoed by Jack's mother-in-law's sentiments exactly. So after all the horrors of war, he found himself home in an unwelcoming and miserable Scotland with no job, no money and the disapproval of his wife's family. Rarely, therefore, did he accompany Ina and little Kitty on their visits to her family, and instead he would sometimes return to Inverness to visit his father, mother and two sisters. Very rarely would Ina accompany him.

As for Ina, although they had been married for nearly seven years, she did not really know her husband. When she had met him in the autumn of 1916, she had quickly fallen for the young man in the Lovat Scouts uniform. However, other than being impressed by the whole romance of being in love with this charming Irish soldier, she had known very little about him, nor he of her.

Throughout the War, she and Kitty had stayed with her mother and sisters in Blackhall, but now, while the Waugh family was soon to be moving to a new 'flatted villa' in St Albans Road in the Grange, the Flannery family had planned to be moving to Shore Cottage, a small 18th-century cottage in Cramond. On first glance this cottage promised to be a romantic little love nest in the slumberous peace of the beautifully unspoilt village overlooking the harbour and Cramond Island, the only companionable sound being that of the water lapping against the boats. However, in reality, Shore Cottage had turned out to be a cramped, damp dwelling, later to be deemed uninhabitable and, along with 25 other such cottages, was demolished not long after the Flannerys had stayed there.

As if these hardships were not enough, Kitty was nearly six years old when her father returned home for good and viewed him as a stranger. Although she should have been at school, her mother had made the excuse that she was 'a delicate child', the dreaded polio having been suspected a couple of times when Kitty had suffered from a sore throat, a fever, a headache and vomiting. Certainly, polio was the world's most feared disease at that time, now that the influenza scare was over, and Ina, like many mothers, was worried that her child would become a victim, although Kitty never actually suffered from stiffness in her neck or anywhere else for that matter. Perhaps Ina was genuinely afraid for her daughter's health, but she was also well aware there was no money with which to send Kitty to George Watson's Ladies' College, which she and Chrissie had attended.

The greatest problem, however, was not the lack of a job, nor the lack of finance for Kitty's education, nor even the constant disapproval of Waugh family. It was the disappearance of any attraction Jack and Ina had once held for each other. Having spent such a short time together before being married in 1916, they had hardly any time to get to know each other and now they were together again they found they had few interests in common, except their daughter. As a result, they spent much of their time apart.

Most evenings, Jack was to be found in the nearby Cramond Inn in the company of fellow unemployed ex-soldiers, who had also done 'their bit' for their country but now were no longer needed. Sadly, he discovered he had more in common with these people than with his wife but, unfortunately, by spending so much time in the Inn, he was in danger of becoming the worth-less Irish drunk described in the Reverend White's report.

With her husband in the pub most evenings, Ina stayed in the cottage, for she could not leave Kitty alone and, while she sat by the fireside listening to the radio and knitting, she became ever more accustomed to enjoying a drink herself for comfort.

One balmy August evening, Ina, at home as usual, was busy wrapping Kitty's present for her sixth birthday. She had chosen to give her the newly-published book entitled, 'The Velveteen Rabbit' by Margery Williams, the story of a toy rabbit and his quest to become real. She was sure the little girl would love it with its magical coloured pictures.

While carefully wrapping the gift, she listened to Al Jolson singing 'Toot Tootsie Goodbye' and other songs. She already possessed a number of records of his, namely 'April Showers' and 'Swanee', and now, rumour had it, perhaps in the next few years a talking picture would be made in which he would star and sing. What an amazing miracle that would be. When it was made, she vowed she would go into town and see the picture at a cinema, but until then she would make do with her records. While thinking this, she picked up her glass of gin and took a sip. When the song came to an end, she then shuffled across to the record player and put 'Look for the Silver Lining' on the turntable. After another quick sip, she began singing along with it to cheer herself up.

Just then the door of the room opened and Jack entered, clutching a large parcel which he put on the table. Then he discarded its wrappings to reveal a beautiful china doll with eyes which opened and closed. How proud he was of his purchase for, despite his lack of money, he had managed to save enough to buy the gift for his daughter's birthday. In his enthusiasm, he turned and tried to kiss his wife, but she turned away from him, finding the whisky fumes from his breath distasteful, while at the same time being ignorant of the fumes of gin on her own.

"How much did that cost you and where did you get it?"

"Does it matter? Kitty will love it. I wonder what she will call it."

"How can you spend money like that when you are unemployed? You can ill afford to squander money when you have no job, although you always seem to find the means for your drams."

"And I suppose it's all right for you to sit here every night with your tipple by your side. How dare you find fault with my drinking. At least I am not swaying about. You are a disgrace. Look, you can't even wrap that present properly."

"Don't speak to me like that. Are you ever going to be a man and get a job to support your family, or are you just going to carry on drinking your life away with your mates in the pub?"

Jack ignored the remark and pulled a newspaper out of his pocket.

"Strangely enough, I think I have the answer. Look at this."

He handed her the paper and she reluctantly sat down to read it. It told of the Empire Settlement Act which offered state-assisted emigration to a variety of countries in the Empire. The article explained that agents had already been sent from Canada to Inverness and Glasgow to offer free travel and work out there for skilled and educated Scots.

"What do you make of that then? We could start a new life there."

"Canada? You expect Kitty and me to go off to the back of beyond just like that? You must be mad."

"But it's a new world with the opportunity of work. It only takes around a week to make the steam crossing to Halifax. Many people are going. We could be with them. If you read the whole of that article, you'll see that one in seven of us here in this country is unemployed and it doesn't look as if it's going to get better. Why don't we take the chance? It's an opportunity not to be missed and we can easily return if the venture's unsuccessful."

"I am not going to leave Edinburgh and my family. And what about Kitty? She needs to be properly educated. Do they have any schools over there, and if so what are they like?"

"You don't seem to be doing too much to help her in that field at the moment," he muttered.

Ina glared at him, downed the rest of the tumbler of gin, and threw the paper down on the table. Then she turned and in as sober a manner as she was able, she bared her teeth and snarled, "How dare you! My mother was right. You are a no-good Irish Catholic: lazy, drunken and a waste of space. Perhaps the Rev. White was right too. Perhaps your kind should be deported. You go if you like – I'll be glad to see the back of you – but one thing is clear. Kitty and I are not going with you. You'll be on your own!"

Jack froze for a moment in disbelief. Then he slowly picked up the newspaper and, with one last look at the doll on the table, made his way to the door.

He never did see the joy on his little girl's face when she opened her Daddy's present on her sixth birthday. Nor did he ever know she named it Daphne, for he was never to see his daughter or his wife again.

Chapter 3

1924: A Will

The scissors somersaulted several times before finding their mark on her neck. Leaving a large scar, they dropped to the floor. The sisters stood aghast at what they had just witnessed, for their great aunt's portrait had always taken pride of place in their home. Now it hung there above the mantelpiece as usual, but with a large tear in its canvas.

They had gathered together that spring morning in their new home in St Albans Road to hear the contents of their mother's will. Chrissie had passed away at the age of 76, having managed to purchase the house before her death. She, like many others, had been a victim of the influenza epidemic although it was less virulent by then, and now she lay in her grave in Bathgate Cemetery beside her estranged husband, her parents and her children.

Her nephews, George Anderson Miller from Perth and Lewis Bilton from Edinburgh, now both Writers to the Signet, had advised the family over the years over legal matters, and that very afternoon had been sitting in the drawing room on uncomfortable but stylish Queen Anne chairs sipping a polite cup of tea, but now they had left. The sisters then moved through to the living room at the back of the house to relax round the fire.

The dining table and chairs sat at one side while the chaise longue lay in front of the window, Chrissie's violin sitting waiting for her to return and play it. Various family portraits hung on the walls, one being that of their famous ancestor Mungo Park. In the centre of the mantelpiece stood an ormolu clock with two 'Wally Dugs' at either end, and above it hung the now damaged painting of Jessie Dickson Turner. She had been the lady of whom all the family had been in awe, and there she was, dressed in her usual rich black satin crinoline, mutch on head, sending out a disapproving stare from her watery beady eyes. Now, however, the painting sported a large tear in the canvas at her neck for Ina, having spied the portrait on entering the room, had immediately picked up a pair of scissors lying on the table and in fury had hurled it at the portrait.

She and her sisters had just learned the contents of their mother's estate, which included the conditions of the Turner Trust that had been set up by the wealthy great aunt, some 20 years before. Most of the details were already known by the sisters such as, that on her death, this wealthy old lady had left quite substantial sums of money to her various nephews and nieces, but for their mother a trust had been set up by which she could only receive the interest on the legacy, and that on her death that interest was to be divided between her daughters. Great Aunt Jessie had so disliked Allan Waugh, their father, and knowing he had lived beyond his means and was usually in debt, she set up this trust to avoid his being able to gain any of her estate. What the sisters did not know until that morning, however, was that, while the yearly interest would now be shared between them, this would only apply to the unmarried sisters. Ina would receive nothing.

On hearing the news and being incandescent with rage, she had struck the portrait. She of all of the sisters needed the money. They all had jobs and owned houses, while she had nothing and had Kitty to provide for. Yet again, fortune had dealt her a poor hand and here she was now being penalised for having married, although that had proved to be a disaster.

What she had not noted in her anger was that the other condition of the trust stipulated that, when all the unmarried sisters died, the actual lump sum would be inherited by any surviving children of the next generation. As Kitty was the only one, she would therefore be the sole benefactor.

Having done the damage, Ina froze in front of the portrait. Was that where she herself had gone wrong? Had she been stupid enough to marry for love and was now being punished? Was this her reward for being so naive? Had her stupidity caused her to be without a decent home of her own, without a husband and with all the scorn of her family heaped upon her?

Even her own daughter seemed to be drifting away from her now that she had begun to attend George Watson's Ladies' College. The school was in George Square and on the south side of town, much easier for her to be picked up by one of her aunts and taken back to St Albans Road than having to go all the way to Cramond, where Ina and Kitty were still living. This arrangement had become more and more frequent and now Ina suspected that her daughter preferred being with her aunts as they spoiled her and gave in to her every whim. She also suspected Kitty preferred the genteel lives found in the Grange.

At last, Georgina slowly turned from the portrait, and tried to march out of the room into the hallway, but not before staggering over a stool on her way. She then looked up at her four sisters who were still stunned by her actions.

"Damn you. Damn you all to hell, you arrogant dried up old witches. At least I've known what it was to love and be loved. You can only dream about it, and none of you will ever know the thrill of being loved by a man. Enjoy your little inheritances. They won't ever make up for your loss."

With that she faced them with a final smirk of hate, staggered passed the four women dressed in mourning attire and banged the front door behind her.

Her sisters stood as if frozen to the spot. One by one, they slowly turned to one another, each wondering what would happen next. Certainly, their sister had always possessed a fiery temper, but more and more they suspected her behaviour was caused by something more. Not that any of them would share their suspicions with the others, but they all suspected she was becoming reliant on strong drink. Alcohol had never entered their home and none of them had ever tasted it, but they recognised the signs and the smell of gin on their sister's breath.

While shocked at Ina's behaviour, each of them nevertheless had sympathy for her. They knew that life had not been easy for her beginning with the death of their brother, Allan. But they were all equally aware of her responsibilities for her little seven-year-old daughter. Their mother, before dying, had made sure Kitty would at least have the opportunity of a good education at George Watson's Ladies' College by arranging to pay her fees, with the understanding that the sisters would continue to do so when she died. However, it was the time when Kitty was neither at school nor with them at St Albans Road that caused them most worry.

Meanwhile, having left the house, Ina rushed along St Albans Road and into Blackford Avenue as fast as she was able, heading for the peace of a bench beside Blackford Pond. Shaking and pent up with anger, she now strongly needed a drink and so opened her handbag and took out a flask, for there was still time for a swig before meeting Kitty from school.

How dare these sanctimonious sisters of hers be granted this legacy, while she herself was excluded! How dare she be deprived! She, the one who had a child to support, was left with nothing, not even a husband to provide for her! What had she done to deserve such a fate?

Where was Jack now anyway, she wondered? Did he not at least want to see Kitty? What kind of a father and husband was he to have left them that fateful August night last year? Had he found another woman? Where had it all gone wrong? What was she to do with her life? She was lonely and no one seemed to care. All that her mother and sisters had ever done was to continually find fault with her. The only comfort she had now was in taking a little 'tipple'. Well, what was the harm in that?

Soon she was seated by the pond, in the peace of the surrounding trees and watching the ducks, some swimming by, others preening themselves on the bank. How much easier to be a duck, she thought, than a human being. All you had to do was make sure you had enough to eat, keep yourself clean and enjoy swimming around in the company of the other ducks. Lucky them.

She looked across to Blackford Hill. Spring had now arrived and the air was warm. It seemed so long ago since she and Jack had climbed the hill. It had been on one of the few days she had spent with Jack before he had set off for Palestine. Everything had been idyllic that day and life had seemed so promising. Certainly, the horror of war was constantly on everyone's minds no matter how friendly and happy people seemed, but, on that day so long ago, Jack and she had been young and optimistic, fully believing they had their lives before them to enjoy together. If life had gone on as it should have, they might have become two of the 'Bright Young Things' she was always reading about and seeing in the cinema. They might have been dancing the night away to the jazz of Louis Armstrong or King Oliver, while learning the steps of the foxtrot, American tango, Charleston or whatever the latest craze was. They might have attended the Grafton Assembly Rooms in Tollcross or the Plaza Salon de Danse in Morningside. She might even have become a 'flapper', sipping cocktails at the Cafe Royal and smoking cigarettes from a long cigarette holder. Yes, she might have been a sensation.

Instead, life had taken a very different turn and here she was alone at 34. Her birthday had been the week before and not one person had sent her a card. Surely, she deserved more than this.

As for Jack's family, although she had tried contacting them several times, she had met them only once and now that their son had disappeared, they didn't seem to be interested in her or Kitty. Perhaps they had been too hurt in losing Jack that they were unable to cope with seeing their granddaughter again. She remembered Major Flannery as an elderly gruff man who had made it quite apparent he did not approve of the marriage. Mrs Flannery, his second wife, seemed a gentle and warm-hearted lady but, like all good wives, she would not have gone against the wishes of her husband. Ina had met Jack's sister, Eileen, but not his younger one, Doreen, about whom there had been a tragic story. When she was studying at Edinburgh University, she had met and had fallen in love with an Indian gentleman but the relationship had been brought to a hasty end thanks to the intervention of her father and the university principal. Since then, she had never talked again and was now in an asylum.

Jack must have been a great disappointment to his parents, disappearing as he did. They had seemed so proud of their handsome young son who had fought so bravely at Gallipoli along with his father. However, the Flannerys had other sons and perhaps they invested more hope in them. Anyhow, they had made it quite clear to Ina that they did not want to keep in touch.

Neither did Ina have any friends. She had lost contact with those from her schooldays for, when she had married, most of them had reacted in the same way as her own family. When she did bump into them in the street, they behaved so awkwardly and she knew she would no longer be welcome in their homes. How narrow-minded these smug and self-satisfied women were. Most of them would now be married to respectable doctors or lawyers, living in their respectable middle class Morningside or Grange homes with their live-in maids, or at least their dailies, to do the chores. They would no doubt be in the habit of changing their dress after lunch every afternoon, in order to be presentable for guests who might arrive before their children came home from one of the Merchant Company schools.

Just one more little 'tipple', she decided, before making her way to George Square. How she despised everything she had been taught at that school and the people who sent their children there. However, her mother had insisted on Kitty's being a pupil and, poor little thing, because of her surname, she was already nick-named 'Flannel Feet'. It was strange seeing Kitty dressed in the maroon uniform she herself had once worn as a 'George Square Gal'.

As the liquor began coursing through her veins, making her feel warmer and more relaxed, she began to remember when she and Chrissie would make their way to school every morning from that happy flat in Warrender Park Road, and how Jessie would make sure they ate their porridge before putting on their blazers and caps. And of course, she would never forget Allan being there too, a dashing young medical student, and how sometimes they had played games, while at others they would visit places like the Museum in Chamber Street, the Castle, Holyrood Palace or the Botanical Gardens. But the particular favourite haunt of theirs had been the zoo at Corstorphine, where they marvelled at the big cats and never tired of watching the chimpanzees' tea party.

But all that had come to an end the day Allan died, and something had died within her too. She had worshipped her brother and, when he had died, she never returned to school. How she wished he was still alive now. She was sure he would never have forgotten her birthday. How she wanted to be in contact with him again. A few years before, she had even contemplated going to one of these séances that took place around Edinburgh. She had read about them and knew that Sir Arthur Conan Doyle, the inventor of Sherlock Holmes, was a great believer and had even given a lecture on spiritualism in the Usher Hall. She would have attended one of these had she had a companion to go with and had thought of asking Chrissie to accompany her, but then changed her mind for Chrissie would have thought it foolish. And so, she never did try to make contact with Allan.

As she sat there she suddenly remembered she did have a friend. Tom. Jack had introduced her to a very attractive young lawyer's apprentice, before the war, but now he was a fully qualified man of the law. She had met Tom again by chance on going into town one day, first to look for a book in the Boots' Booklovers

Library on Princes Street and then to Patrick Thompsons on the Bridges for afternoon tea, where she bumped into him again. Now married and living in Marchmont, Tom was working in Falkirk but they arranged to meet again and continued to do so, sometimes for a coffee or tea at McVities or Jenners. Sometimes they would even attend a cinema or share a few cocktails in the North British Hotel.

Ina knew Tom was married but he had explained to her that his marriage was virtually over and that soon he would be divorced. She therefore continued seeing him for she enjoyed his company and he knew how to treat a lady. Of course, her sisters knew nothing of her friend, nor indeed did Kitty. Tom was her little secret.

Realising it was getting late, she had one more 'tipple', put the flask away in her bag and took out her lipstick and compact. She carefully outlined her lips in scarlet, patted her nose with a puff of powder and then, after putting the cosmetics back in her handbag, she took out a peppermint sweet and put it in her mouth. She did not want her daughter to think she had been drinking, although Kitty had sometimes commented on the smell of gin on her mother's breath when she had given her a kiss.

Finally drawing herself up to her full height and holding her head up high, Ina then walked along the side of the pond, and while admiring the spring daffodils, she left the ducks to their own devices.

Chapter 4

1932: A Punishment

The chimes of Big Ben rang out from the wireless. The epilogue from Westminster Abbey had just ended and 1932 had begun. This was followed by dance music with such songs as 'Dancing in the Dark' and 'As Time Goes By', great hits from the previous year played by Jack Payne and the BBC Dance Band. But in most Scottish homes the wireless was now turned off, for friends and families throughout the land were joining hands to sing 'Auld Lang Syne' and to wish each other "A Happy New Year".

In Drumbrae Road, North Barnton, neighbours were also laughing and drinking with their loved ones. But not so in number 31. In that house lay a lone figure on the floor, oblivious to the celebrations around the country. Ina had drunk herself into a stupor and was now lying comatose, having fallen off her chair and hit the ground. For her, there were no friends or family with whom to celebrate Hogmanay, for no one would venture near the home of such a pathetic, drunk and fallen woman.

Despite not receiving any financial support from the Turner Trust when her mother had died eight years before, Ina had discovered she had been left enough money from her mother's estate to buy herself a house. The sisters also contributed a sum to the purchase.

She had chosen a bungalow in Barnton with two public rooms, three bedrooms, one bathroom and a kitchen with electric light and pleasant gardens to look out on both front and back. It was a new build, one of many constructed around that time in Edinburgh to house the growing population for, despite the chronic unemployment throughout Scotland, there were still many people, clerks, tradesmen and shopkeepers, able to buy suburban homes such as here in Barnton and Corstorphine.

While being excited at the prospect of owning such a home, she had been particularly delighted at having a streetlamp right outside the door. Although the principal streets in the centre of town were now lit by electric lamps, Barnton's streets were still lit by gas, and whenever she saw the lamplighter coming round to light the lamps at dusk, she always thought of Robert Louis Stevenson's poem 'The Lamplighter' which she used to read to Kitty. While in the poem the lamplighter carried a ladder to reach the wick, all that was needed now was a long pole to access the pilot light.

Ina had named her home 'Ingleneuk' for the word promised cosiness and secrecy. It seemed an ideal name for a love nest, her relationship with Tom having become more serious. While he still worked in Falkirk during the week, they managed to spend much of the time together, when he was not at home with his wife.

For Kitty, however, it had been a truly upsetting situation to be in. Although often at St Albans Road with her aunts, she had still lived with her mother but, when a lover arrived in her mother's life, she had resented his presence. She had hated his smooth ways, and her mother's flirtatious behaviour she found quite distasteful. Eventually she had shared her feelings with her Auntie Chrissie who, along with her sisters, was horrified at the situation.

It was bad enough having to endure the humiliation of having a drunken, fallen woman in the family, but now for someone to be committing adultery was unforgiveable. No one in the family had ever behaved so shamefully. How relieved they were that at least their mother had been spared such scandal. Something had to be done. They had already known how Kitty had been ridiculed at school for wearing unkempt, unclean and un-ironed blouses, thanks to her mother's lack of care, but this was something different. Quite swiftly they had agreed that it was time to intervene on the child's behalf and take full charge of their niece.

Initially, Ina would not accept the proposals made by her sisters to bring Kitty up in their house, but finally she had had to admit it would make life simpler and so eventually and reluctantly she agreed. She had known it would be the best arrangement for everyone, but she had also known she would miss her daughter's company. They had enjoyed time together attending theatres and cinemas and had spent many pleasant evenings watching such films as 'The Jazz Singer' and marvelling at being able to hear a soundtrack for the first time. They had also shared an interest in clothes. How Kitty had longed to wear the latest fashions, dance to the latest tunes of the day and see the latest films. All these interests they shared.

But Ina also believed that, over the years, Kitty had been spoiled by her sisters. Although Alice was a health visitor living in South Queensferry and Minnie ran her own nursing home in Selkirk, whenever they visited Edinburgh they would always provide the girl with some treat or other. Meanwhile, Jessie and Chrissie would take her to Greensmith Downe's in George Street, J R Allan's on the Bridges or Wilkie's in Shandwick Place to buy her the latest fashionable new clothes. Sometimes, Chrissie would take her to a picture house to see a film or hear a concert in the Usher Hall. Ina was well aware of her sister's accomplishments as a violinist, as Chrissie's name was quite often mentioned in the 'Evening News'. She was becoming quite a well-known amateur solo violin performer and had played in such places as the Central Hall at Tollcross and the Guthrie Memorial Hall in Easter Road.

Ina herself had never been keen on classical music, although she had learned to play the piano as a child. Both she and Kitty had preferred popular music and jazz. Kitty had never been particularly interested in playing an instrument, but she had enjoyed singing. Ina would never forget the day Kitty, having returned from seeing Marlene Dietrich in 'The Blue Angel', had wandered round the house singing 'Falling in Love Again', while trying to look glamorous and mysterious with her long legs and sultry expression. When not trying to be the German femme fatale, Kitty would try giving an impression of the 'Swedish Sphinx', Greta Garbo, whom she had seen in 'Grand Hotel'. Now that film stars could be heard, Kitty loved trying out a Swedish accent while repeating the star's famous line from 'Anna Christy', "Gimme a whisky, ginger ale on the side, and don't be stingy, baby".

While sitting in a still and poised manner in front of her bedroom mirror, Kitty would attempt to adopt Garbo's soulful eyes. Ina herself had admired the star's beauty, her perfect, flawless complexion and bone structure but she knew that she herself was no longer beautiful and she envied Kitty her youth.

Perhaps Ina would later regret her decision to part with Kitty, but life at that time had been exciting. Tom had been wary of being seen with her in public as he had his reputation to keep up and did not want his young son to know of his clandestine relationship, and so he and Ina would go out of town for entertainment to such places as Peebles Hydro. There they would dine and dance, he in his immaculate evening suit, white scarf and kid gloves, and she in a fetching low-backed evening dress 'a la Garbo'. How she adored these evenings.

Sometimes they had dared to spend Sundays in Edinburgh, walking in the Botanical Gardens, or had taken the tramcar to Portobello where he had been born. There they would enjoy the long stretch of beach and watch the children on the donkeys. She had loved returning on the top deck of a tram, while listening to the switch of the electric pole on the overhead wires and watching the sparks.

Some evenings they would visit a cinema. He had taken her to the New Victoria cinema in Clark Street when it opened. She had longed to see its auditorium reported in the 'Evening News' as being designed to represent a Greek amphitheatre with its colonnades, statues, Corinthian columns and starlight ceiling. Just before Christmas, they had gone to see Charlie Chaplin in 'City Lights' and, at the end of an evening, after a walk along Princes Street, Tom had hired a taxi from the fleet of imposing cars lined up just below the castle to take them home.

However, no longer having her daughter's company and, while still enjoying the precious weekends with Tom, the days of the week were lonely and endless. To alleviate the boredom during the day, Ina would visit dress shops and buy expensive clothes such as a black corded silk coat with Persian lamb collar edged with white fur, or a hemp straw hat with lace and rosebuds on the brim. She would visit Lipton's and, as well as purchasing her usual groceries such as corned beef, custard powder, rice and prunes, she would also make sure she had gin, whisky and sherry in the house.

In the evenings, she had felt particularly lonely and would listen to plays and news on the wireless. Although not terribly interested in current affairs, she had been aware that in October 1929 the US stock market had crashed, and that America's economy collapsed causing mayhem throughout the world. She had also learned how the industrial region of Glasgow had taken the brunt of the crisis; that the ship building and cargo shipping industries there had suffered, bringing unemployment and poverty to many. In Edinburgh jobs were scarce too, and no one could be unaware of the growing slum communities. She had read somewhere that nearly seven million people in Britain had been on the dole.

As the news had been so depressing, she had preferred to sit by her fire and read books such as those by F. Scott Fitzgerald or D. H. Lawrence and, as she discovered these other worlds, she had imagined herself as one of the guests at a Gatsby party or with

Gudrun and Ursula at one given by Hermione Roddice. All the time she sat with these novels, she would quietly sip, not the fun cocktails described in the books, but her usual gin. More than once, she had woken up the following morning to find she had spent the night passed out in her chair.

In time, 'Ingleneuk' became less cared for and slowly Ina paid less and less attention to what she ate or what she wore. Eventually, she had become aware of her dwindling finances and had arranged for Dowell's in George Street to organise a private sale of some of her furniture, including the piano on which Kitty had practised.

Eventually, after all the days of fun and flirtation, Tom could no longer handle her behaviour and no longer found her attractive. He therefore called an end to their relationship and, despite Ina's tears and pleas, he had packed his bags and left. Ina was abandoned once again.

Now, on that first day of 1932, she lay on the floor, an upturned glass beside her, its contents long since soaked into the carpet while, on the nearby table, sat an empty bottle of gin. Beside it lay a letter which had been there for several weeks. It was from the bank informing her that she was in debt and, no longer being able to afford to live in her house, it was advising Ina to sell up and move out as fast as possible.

Chapter 5

1939: An Outsider

Edinburgh had always been a city of two halves and, although Ina rarely visited the High Street or the Canongate, she found herself there for a particular occasion, and witnessed the grinding poverty. She saw men and women, accompanied by their shoeless children, singing for pennies in the street; ex-servicemen playing on their banjos, concertinas, guitars, ukuleles, fiddles, spoons and even paper and combs churning out old favourite songs such as 'The Old Rugged Cross' or war songs such as 'It's a Long Way to Tipperary', their proffered upturned military caps lying beside them. Some of these old soldiers, roughly clad and looking ill-fed, often blind or missing an arm or leg, would be proudly wearing their war medals, still waiting for 'a land fit for heroes'. Ina thought of Jack and wondered what had become of him.

The previous May, all the beggars had been cleared from the High Street, for King George and Queen Mary were to visit. Ina had joined the cheering crowds who were lining the street and waving their flags as the royal couple had passed in their open carriage drawn by two white horses, on their way up the Royal Mile from Holyrood Palace to attend a service at St Giles. The King, with his neatly pointed beard, wore a plumed hat and decorated uniform, while his queen was resplendent in white, wearing a stylish toque hat for which she had become famous.

The pomp and ceremony of the occasion brought forth the pillars of Edinburgh society, the magistrates, constables, politicians and the city's Lord Provost, some in wigs and fine ermine, making their way to the Cathedral, accompanied by the sound of bagpipes. It was a sight never to be forgotten. No beggars were to be seen that day for there was to be no reminder of how the country had failed its brave soldiers. But by the next day everything was back to normal and the usual inhabitants were again emerging from their slum abodes.

On arriving in the Royal Mile, Ina decided to position herself at the foot of the Mercat Cross where she could mingle with the tourists and not be conspicuous. Parliament Square had always attracted many visitors to the nucleus of old Edinburgh, for it had long been the heart of the city's religious and legal life, with St Giles Cathedral looming over the square on one side and the courts on the other. Many proclamations had been made over the centuries from the Mercat Cross and many executions had been carried out. These public hangings and beheadings had taken place in front of crowds of sometimes over 2,000 people and, although the original building had been replaced by a larger monument in the 19th century, the times of the once three daily executions were still displayed.

Ina stood in front of this monument and while waiting she watched passers-by spitting for good luck on the heart-shaped mosaic on the cobblestones. This was known as the Heart of Midlothian, the exact spot where the old Tolbooth, the prison, had once stood, and where many an unfortunate had been hanged. Deacon Brodie, the well-respected town councillor by day and crook by night, had breathed his last in that very place.

John Porteous had not been so lucky. He had been the captain of the guard who, in trying to quell the riot in the Grass-market at the execution of two smugglers, had ordered his men to fire above the crowd's heads but, unfortunately, in doing so several inhabitants who had been hanging out of the windows to watch the proceedings had been shot. For this unfortunate event, Porteous had been imprisoned in the Tolbooth but his end had come, not at the Mercat Cross, but in the Grassmarket when the crowd had seized him from prison and made him suffer an even more tortuous death.

Ina shivered as she imagined the expectant crowds of yester-year gathering where she stood. She could almost hear the nearby Cathedral bell ringing as the executions took place. Today, however, as on every day, visitors were taking pictures and going in and out of the Cathedral where John Knox had given many fiery sermons railing against Catholicism and his queen, Mary Queen of Scots.

She looked up and down the Royal Mile, once referred to as the "highway of agony and ecstasy" with its looming, menacing Castle at the top and the Renaissance beauty of Holyrood Palace at the bottom, its having also been compared to a fish's spine with its many closes and wynds leading off it. For many years these closes, many stinking ravines, had been crammed with tenements teeming with life and where, during the bubonic plague, the inhabitants had died like flies. It was also the place where many a so-called witch had been routed out and taken to the Nor' Loch to prove her guilt or innocence. Those that drowned being deemed innocent and those who floated were guilty and were then punished by burning at the stake.

From the top of Castlehill, the old cannon, Mons Meg, would daily signal one o'clock, while in the Lawnmarket at the other end of the Royal Mile, originally called 'land market', stalls would sell produce from the country. Later, however, it was given the title of 'lawn market' as it became famous for its excellent cloth on sale.

Edinburgh had always been referred to as the 'Athens of the North' for it was here the intellectual flowering of the 18th century had bloomed. David Hume, Adam Smith, the economist; Alan Ramsay, the artist; Robert Ferguson, the poet; not to mention Sir

Walter Scott, had walked this street. Even Robert Burns had been there, while flirting with his fair 'Clarinda', Mrs Nancy Maclehose.

By 1939, although the New Town in contrast was prosperous, the inhabitants of the Old Town were still tightly packed into filthy, crowded dwellings situated off the narrow closes off the Royal Mile. The poverty, disease and decay of the past were still there. Ina watched some ragged, barefooted boys playing 'peevers' with the chalk numbers drawn on the pavement and dexterously skimming an old empty tobacco tin from square to square, while others, crouching in the gutter, played marbles. Across the road, she saw some girls skipping with a rope tied to the end of a drainpipe and taking it in turns to caw the rope while the others would skip in and out chanting "Salt, Mustard, Vinegar, Pepper". It brought back memories of Ina's own childhood, only then she had been skipping in the well-tended gardens of George Square.

All these sights were unfamiliar to Ina. She was more used to those of Princes Street and George Street with their bustling tea shops like Mackie's or McVitie's, or the various department stores such as Smalls, Forsyth's, Darling's or Binn's, not to mention the luxurious Jenner's.

But that day she had not come to idle away her time dreaming of Edinburgh's past. She had come to witness a newly-married couple soon to be emerging from the Sheriff Court House. This was her second visit to the spot in one week. The first had been to see her once-beloved lawyer lover, Tom, who, having finally managed to obtain a divorce from his wife, had married a respectable 32-year-old Falkirk spinster. His young lady had managed to acquire the role Ina had coveted but she had always known that that would never to be possible. She would forever be married to Jack Flannery, until proved otherwise. How she cursed him for leaving her the way he did, for she could never marry again. Her only option had been to live as someone's mistress, thus forever marking her out by society as a 'wicked' woman.

When she discovered Tom was to be married again, the very next month after obtaining his divorce papers, Ina had arranged to be outside the Midlothian County Buildings in the High Street to see her former lover and his attractive young wife emerge as husband and wife. Sadly Ina was now nearly 50, and the years of alcohol dependence had taken their toll. Over the years, Ina had often wondered if she had made a bad choice in not going to Canada with Jack. But that was long ago and now it was too late.

She then thought back on the years after her Tom had exited from her life. Being in debt, she had managed to sell 'Ingleneuk'. There she had to face the grim reality of surviving through the days of the Depression when jobs were hard to come by. However, she had made a determined effort to curb the drinking and had worked in various Edinburgh hotels, staying mostly in these hotels or in boarding houses nearby.

Now here she was once more, only one week later, standing again across the road from the same building to witness a second wedding. This time it was that of her daughter, Kitty. Over the years her sister, Chrissie, had kept in touch and had from time to time given her money to pay the bills. She had also always kept her informed of Kitty's life. Her daughter had chosen to have nothing more to do with her, and according to Chrissie, the young girl's life had turned out well, having spent a happy childhood in the care of her aunts. She had enjoyed the company of many school friends, as well as that of the boys and girls who lived in St Albans Road. She had been taken by her aunt on many wonderful holidays both at home and abroad – to Jersey, the Isle of Man, Scarborough, Belgium, Holland and France. At 15, Chrissie had also taken Kitty to Inverness to visit her grandparents, Major Flannery and his wife. They had been overjoyed to meet their young granddaughter after all these years but had heard no word of Jack. They had always wondered if he had joined the French Foreign Legion. Now sadly, the old soldier was dead and had gone to his grave, ignorant of what had happened to this precious son of his with whom he had fought so gallantly at Gallipoli.

Kitty, it seemed, had enjoyed being a schoolgirl at 'George Square' and Chrissie had shown Ina many school photos of her daughter from when she was young with her long ringlets, to when older with her short fashionable hairstyle, no doubt still wanting to resemble Garbo. It had been obvious from the pictures that Kitty, dressed in her school blouse, tie and gym slip or in her school swimsuit at Portobello Beach, spent a happy childhood with many school friends and, in her final year at school, was made Dux for secretarial subjects. There she had attended Dugdales College in Abercrombie Place to train as a secretary. Throughout the years, while excelling at games and particularly in swimming, her favourite sport had been ice skating and at least twice a week she had attended Haymarket Ice Rink. There she had met David Somerville. He had been born in Australia but brought up in Johannesburg, South Africa, his father working there as a metallurgist in a gold mine. At 12, he was brought to Scotland to attend Edinburgh Institution, or Melville College as it was later called, his father having been educated there himself. And so, in 1931, he and his younger brother, Jack, sailed with their parents from South Africa via Accra to Southampton and then on to Scotland and Edinburgh to settle into 'digs' in Montague Terrace. While David had enjoyed school, his younger brother had not and had returned to Johannesburg to complete his education.

David grew into a strikingly attractive and very tall young man who excelled at rugby, for which he won a school cap. Chrissie had described to Ina how comical he had looked when, at six-foot-two tall, he had had to wear shorts as was decreed by the school, no matter how tall its pupils grew.

But, as well as playing rugby, the young lad had also had a great love for ice skating and, shortly after arriving in Edinburgh, had gone to the Haymarket Ice Rink. There he had soon met Kitty. From then on, they had learned to dance together and enjoyed each other's company both on and off the ice.

As he and Kitty became closer, he had begun to appear

regularly at St Albans Road and stayed for meals. The aunts grew fond of the lad as time progressed and found him to be a humorous and caring young man who dealt bravely with the situation, being so far from home and from his family in South Africa.

After his sixth year, he left school and went on to study mining engineering at Heriot Watt College, as had his father, and continued visiting the aunts from his 'digs' in 35 Warrender Park Road. Chrissie found his address quite a coincidence, for it was only 'a stone's throw' from where she and Ina had lived as schoolgirls at number 25 all those years ago. But now, with his course coming to an end and Britain facing war once more, he and Kitty, like many couples, had decided to marry. It was the 15th November 1939.

Suddenly, there was some activity at the door of the Sheriff Court, and into the street came Chrissie, laughing and looking flustered, escorted by a young man, presumably, like herself, a witness to the proceedings. Only after that did Ina see her slim, long-legged and very glamorous daughter emerge. She was accompanied by a dashing, dark-haired young man of some considerable height, who was laughing and helping her into a nearby taxi. Kitty, while holding her warm wool coat close round her, clutched his arm with the other. The veil of her jauntily placed little blue hat could not conceal the sheer joy on the young bride's face. Certainly here were two young people very much in love and ready to face the future, whatever it was to bring.

As the taxis drew up to take the party on their way to celebrate the occasion, Chrissie looked round and caught a glimpse of Ina. She winked at her and Ina remembered how Chrissie had been witness at her own wedding, when she and Jack had been the happy newly-married couple exiting from St Mary's Cathedral. Another time, another place, another war. Now here was Chrissie carrying out the role once again, but this time for Ina's daughter.

When she had last met Chrissie, Ina had asked if there would be any possibility of her meeting Kitty again, but the answer had been very clear: Kitty was adamant that she never ever wanted to see her mother again.

And so, Ina found herself standing there alone on that bleak November day. After the taxis had driven off, she slipped her hand into her handbag and brought out a silver flask. Quickly, she unscrewed the top and held the flask to her lips. With tears running down her face, she toasted the young couple, hoping her daughter's life would be happier than hers.

That was the last time Ina was to see Kitty, except for one more many years later, again at a wedding but held in another city, when she again would be an outsider.

Part 7

Kitty's Story

Chapter 1

8th May 1945: A Celebration

Chocolate! Kitty bit into one of the many hundreds of Hershey bars that were showering down on the assembled crowds from the balcony of the American Red Cross Army Club in Princes Street. Chocolate bars and packs of Wrigley's double mint gum were hastily being opened, the taste of sugar having long been denied everyone for so long, apart from the allocated weekly three-ounce sweet ration. Now things were to change for the War in Europe was finally over. Blackout curtains could be torn down. The sound of sirens and the fear of bombing had come to an end. Rationing of food and clothing would soon disappear, and the lights would come on again. Above all, loved ones would return home. This was Victory in Europe Day, Tuesday 8th May 1945, and everyone was celebrating.

Jubilant crowds gathered in Princes Street despite the inclement weather. Flags were flying from the windows of buildings, Union Jacks dominating but the Scottish Standard, the Stars and Stripes, the French and Belgian national flags, and even the Red Flag of Russia with its golden hammer and sickle, could be seen. Strings of pennants floated in the air, and windowsills and balconies were decked with bunting.

On the balcony of the Club, a lone marine had taken it upon himself to conduct the crowd in the community singing of 'Roll out the Barrel', 'The Yanks are coming' and 'Tipperary'. Everyone sang with such gusto, joining hands or placing arms round shoulders of complete strangers while, in the American fashion, everywhere torn-up paper cascaded down from the windows into the street.

After catching and eating the chocolate, while at the same time filling their pockets with chewing gum, Kitty and Anne decided to make their way towards the east end of the street to the Wellington Statue where another large crowd had gathered on the steps of Register House and on the pavement below. All eyes were on a British soldier perched precariously on the mane of the Duke of Wellington's horse, from where he was trying to catch hats being flung to him. Then other soldiers and sailors climbed onto the statue to join him while, from out of the crowd, around 30 young sailors emerged marching in solemn procession from the Leith direction, each carrying a pint glass. At a word from their leader, they stopped in regimental style, took a drink and then, at another command, moved off down Princes Street, their glasses held high in jubilation.

Kitty had promised to meet her aunt at St Giles Cathedral before 6:30p.m.to attend a service, and so she and Anne made their way up the Mound to where more people were standing singing, but this time the song was 'Land of Hope and Glory'.

Soon they had arrived at the High Street and, when Kitty saw the County Buildings, she was suddenly overwhelmed with a feeling of loss, for she was reminded of her wedding there to David only five years before in November 1939. The following year, having graduated from Heriot Watt College with his degree in Mining Engineering, he had joined the Royal Engineers as Second Lieutenant, the very month their baby son was born and, because of his knowledge of mining, had soon been appointed to the 180 Tunnelling Company and sent to Gibraltar. He was to take part in constructing the Great North Road which would allow lorries to travel from the north to the south entirely within the Rock. An underground bombproof city inside the Rock was also being planned to house 16,000 troops, with enough supplies to last 16 months and which would have facilities such as a telephone exchange, a generating station, a water delineation plant, a hospital, a frozen food store, a bakery and ammunition magazines. It was also planned to have a vast Royal Electrical and Mechanical Engineers shed where damaged vehicles and equipment could be repaired. But David, alas, was never to see these plans come to fruition because on 3rd June 1941 he was blown up and killed on the Rock. His son was not even one year old.

Kitty, not quite 24, had returned to stay with her aunts in St Albans Road bringing her baby, who was, of course, doted on by all. He was named David after his father, but David and Kitty had decided the little boy would be called by his second name, Norman, to avoid confusion later which worked out to be unnecessary.

Much can happen in a short time during war years, and when there is uncertainty about the future, people live their lives at a much quicker pace. Kitty had been no exception. One evening she was persuaded by her three friends, Anne, Veronica and Betty, to attend a dance at the Maybury Hotel in Corstorphine, where she was introduced to Fergie Mackie, a Captain in the Queens Own Cameron Highlanders.

Before the war, Fergie had been a teller in the Commercial Bank in Lochboisdale, a village in South Uist, where he joined the Territorial Army at the outbreak of war, and, from the peaceful life of the Western Isles, soon found himself in a very different one. Like all the other soldiers in the Highland Divisions at the beginning of the war, he went into battle without a gun and only a skean dhu – a knife worn in his sock – to confront the enemy. As for the wearing of underpants under his kilt, the rules of the Division decreed that that item of clothing was disallowed and a mirror was placed on the ground during inspections to check the rule was carried out.

On 11th June 1940, Fergie had found himself with 25,000 other British soldiers at St Valery en Caux making his way to the beaches to embark for home. He arrived as part of the 4th Cameron Highlanders Division in the valley of Neville three miles south of St Valery where the soldiers hid their transport in an orchard near the church and waited for instructions. Luck was on their side through a miscalculation, for the 1st Gordon Highlanders and the 4th Cameron Highlanders swapped places and, while the Camerons waited as ordered at Neville, the Gordons found themselves on the beaches facing the horror of being attacked by Rommel and the Germans. Very many Gordon Highlanders were killed or taken prisoner that day, while most of the Camerons managed to get away, Fergie being one of them. He escaped but had been wounded and so was taken to hospital in La Baule, before finally being evacuated home from Saint Nazaire.

This had happened on the very day Kitty's baby son had been born in Edinburgh, though Kitty had not met Fergie by then. Their meeting didn't take place until 1942, when he was stationed in Edinburgh as adjutant and quartermaster of the 3rd City of Edinburgh Home Guard, and living in a flat in Relugas Road, near St Albans Road with his batman.

Soon he was escorting her to dances, theatres, cinemas and parties and she, while perhaps not actually falling in love with him, appreciated his attentiveness and kindness to herself and her little son. Despite the atrocities Fergie had witnessed, he was always gentle and amiable, popular with people no matter who they were; and after a few months of their knowing one another, Kitty accepted his proposal of marriage. She knew, however, that he would never be the love of her life, and she suspected Fergie knew and understood this too.

They married in the July of that year in the new Reid Memorial Church at the foot of Blackford Avenue near to St Albans Road. Kitty had worn a fox stole over her dress and a jaunty little hat, while Fergie had been in full Highland regalia which included his kilt and sporran. Veronica Hoe, Kitty's friend from schooldays, was her bridesmaid, while Dan Crichton Byrom Bramwell, the grandson of the well-known physician, Sir Byrom Bramwell, was best man. Kitty was still not yet 25 and had already been a wife, a mother, a widow, and now she was to be a wife again.

Then, at the beginning of 1944, she and Fergie had been sitting in the Empire Theatre in South Clark Street watching a variety programme consisting of acts such as Sid Amoy, known as 'the Chinese umbrella man', Adelaide Hill 'the crooning blackbird', and Dick Henderson, the Yorkshire comedian. They were waiting for the highlight of the evening, Troise and his Mandoliers to appear but, just as they began singing 'Just a Song at Twilight', Kitty had to be escorted out of the theatre, put into a taxi and taken quickly to a nursing home in Drumsheugh Gardens. Her second baby was on its way and sometime later, her daughter Sylvia was born.

Now on VE Day, Kitty was hoping the children were sound asleep in St Albans Road. Her Auntie Minnie, although now suffering badly from emphysema having become a heavy smoker during her time in France, was to be left in charge for a short time. Sadly, Kitty's two eldest aunts, Jessie and Alice, had died two years previously.

Fergie was not with them in Edinburgh that day, as he was now a Major in the army and stationed in Zedelgem in Brussels. He was Commandant of No. 2229 P.O.W. Camp and in charge of some of over 15,000 German prisoners whose main hardships were forced labour, hunger, homesickness and boredom, slightly alleviated by organised sporting and cultural activities. Fergie, while home on leave, told Kitty how several of the prisoners whiled away the hours drawing, sculpting and making murals. One had even created caricature drawings on a wall depicting the British officers, and had included one of Fergie portrayed as a happy 'Jock' in kilt and sporran dancing the Highland Fling.

On that day of celebration, Auntie Chrissie was waiting for Kitty and Anne on the steps of the Cathedral, along with many other people, but the three of them managed to find themselves somewhere to sit. Kitty found peace in the ancient place of worship, away from the jubilant throngs outside, for it was cool and comforting. Many in the Cathedral that evening would be giving thanks for the end to the horrors of the War and were there to pay tribute to all the men and women who had fought, and especially to those who had lost their lives during the conflict. Those who had come to worship appeared generally older than those celebrating outside, and Kitty reckoned some could recall being there in 1918, when the congregation had prayed that World War One would be the war to end all wars. Now they would be doing so once more, on that evening in 1945.

When the service came to an end, Auntie Chrissie instructed Kitty to stay in town and enjoy the rest of the evening while she herself would go back home to attend to the children. The older lady then made her way to the station to catch a train back to Blackford Station leaving Kitty and Anne, both of whose husbands were still away from home, to stay behind and celebrate.

Outside the Cathedral in the Canongate, children were lighting bonfires, while others began dancing and singing. Already, earlier that day at the Mercat Cross, there had been a brief ceremony at which the 76th Psalm had been read, the Lord Provost having explained that it had been read in the same place in 1588 as a thanksgiving to God for the defeat of the Spanish Armada. Now he asked the assembled crowd to remember, "Those who have given their lives in this War, those who have suffered and those who mourn." He also asked everyone to "ask God to commit to His gracious keeping those who are very dear to us but who still continue to fight, and pray that in time they will return to us in peace."

The two young women then made their way down the Mound from the High Street to Princes Street Gardens to find the crowds now walking in the streets, for there was no room on the pavements. The rain had stopped and the evening was becoming mild and pleasant. Nobody wanted to stay in and already many pubs and restaurants had closed because of an exhaustion of supplies, which meant the crowds, while jubilant, were mainly sober.

Down in Princes Street Gardens, everyone was dancing to piped music. The familiar voices of the Andrew Sisters, Bing Crosby and Vera Lynn rang out, as did the sound of the big bands such as those of Benny Goodman and Duke Ellington. Even mothers with babies in their arms were joining in the celebrations. A big party had gathered near the Ross Fountain below the Castle, for there a piper was playing his bagpipes while servicemen, factory workers and shop girls, mostly strangers to one another, were dancing eightsome reels with abandonment.

Later in the evening, Kitty and Anne made their way up the Mound once more towards George Square, for it was there that the focal point of the celebrations was to take place. That spacious area, surrounded by fine Georgian houses – many of which had been homes to such celebrities as Lord Braxfield 'the hanging judge', Sir Arthur Conan Doyle and Sir Walter Scott – was quickly becoming a seething mass of humanity, while the mounted police tried hard to keep the thoroughfare free of traffic. Then, at 10.30pm as promised, the illuminations were switched on and the green, red, yellow, white and blue lights began weaving a colourful pattern across trees and monuments.

Everywhere in Edinburgh at that exact moment the street-lights, which had been switched off for so long, were all lit up once again inviting the crowd in George Square and elsewhere to sing 'When the Lights Go on Again'. This was followed by several other wartime songs. The celebrations finally came to an end with two of Vera Lynn's most famous songs, 'The White Cliffs of Dover' and 'We'll Meet Again'.

Kitty had mixed feelings as she stood and joined in the singing on that spring night in 1945. So much had happened for her in such a short a time and, while she was celebrating the end of the War in Europe, she, like many thousands of others, was grieving. She had been married for such a short time to David before he was killed. He had been so young and had never seen his father again, after saying goodbye to him at the age of 12. Mr Somerville never came over to Scotland to visit David; nor did David ever go back to South Africa. The greatest tragedy, however, was that David would never see his own son growing up.

After saying goodnight to Anne, she made her way home alone across the Meadows. As she walked, she remembered how she and David had both loved the songs of Al Bowlly, the South African crooner, who had also been brought up in Johannesburg. The words of their favourite, 'The Very Thought of You', came back to her and she softly began singing,

"The very thought of you and I forget to do
The little ordinary things that everyone ought to do
I'm living in a kind of daydream and I'm as happy as a king
And foolish as it may seem to me it's everything.
The near idea of you, the longing here for you.
You'll never know how slow the moments go until I'm near to you.
I see your face in every flower, your eyes in stars above
It's just the thought of you, the very thought of you, my love."

But Al Bowlly was dead too, having been killed by a Luftwaffe parachute mine that detonated outside his London flat in 1941.

As she continued walking across the Meadows among the crowd also making their way to their homes after the celebrations, she began to wonder what the future would bring. What would the new post-war world be like? No more blackouts. No more telegrams bringing tragic news. More food. More freedom. Peace at last.

She also suspected that with the end of the war she would be saying goodbye to her beloved Edinburgh, for Fergie had always wanted to return north. However, that was somewhere in the future, and so on that evening she carried on singing to herself:

"If today your heart is weary
If every little thing looks grey
Just forget your troubles and learn to say
Tomorrow is a lovely day."

Chapter 2

1957: A Sale

As at the end of the First World War, Britain was again a country of large unemployment. There was a shortage of housing and everyone felt tired and grey. Rationing restricted food to a little sugar, butter, fat and cheese, one egg and two pints of milk per person per week, and even bread was rationed. Winston Churchill, the hero of the people during the War, had been beaten in the general election, and the Labour Party had come into power led by Clement Atlee, who promised "jam tomorrow". But the people wanted it today. It was a country which stood for decency, where people rose when the national anthem played in cinemas at the end of the evening, where birchings and hangings were still used as punishment, where beatings in schools were taken for granted, and where divorce was a scandal, as was the sight of an unmarried mother.

Luckily Fergie did have a job to go to, and returned to his 'civvy job' as a teller in the Commercial Bank at the bottom of Union Street in Aberdeen. Kitty had of course already visited her in-laws in their home at the Bridge of Don, and had met other members of the family. Fergie's father had been a headmaster in various schools in Aberdeenshire and his wife a teacher. Both had retired to Aberdeen and during the War had been involved in placing evacuees in safe homes. These evacuees had come from Edinburgh and Glasgow, although ironically Aberdeen had seen more bombing than the capital. Glasgow, of course, had taken a heavy toll, especially around Clydebank where the ships were built.

While Fergie – always referred to by his parents as Ferguson – was a single child, perhaps something to do with his father being 19 years older than his mother, he had several cousins, uncles and aunts. These relations were in the habit of congregating regularly at the various homes, even going on holiday together, and Kitty tried hard to settle into the sprawling Mackie family. They were all certainly well-educated and hard-working people, but they appeared to regard anyone who did not belong to the locality as inferior. Her mother-in-law had even boasted how she and her husband had come home early from a holiday in London, as she couldn't understand a word they spoke – as if the fault somehow lay with the Londoners.

While waiting for the completion of their new home in Sclattie Park, Bucksburn, then in the county and not the city, Kitty found herself living at the Braes, the house belonging to her in-laws at the Bridge of Don, where each Sunday all the relations would gather to share the latest gossip. She sensed there was much competition between the women in the family and most seemed to have little interest in the wider world. Their talk was largely of children, houses, cooking, baking, sewing and gardening and what they had achieved. To her, they appeared smug and self-satisfied with little interest in theatre, cinema, music, restaurants, fashion or dance tunes. As for taking any interest in what was going on in Edinburgh, it was dismissed as a place full of 'posh' schools and frivolous people without substance – place of "all fur coats and no knickers", whereas they regarded people in the north as diligent, honest and God-fearing. They were the "salt of the earth".

Unlike most of the rest of the family, both of Fergie's parents had attended the 'varsity' in Aberdeen and were rightly proud of their achievements. His mother had been brought up on a small croft, had won a Carnegie bursary in 1905 to attend Aberdeen University at the age of 16. By the time she was 19, she had gained a degree in English, Latin and philosophy plus a teaching qualification. No small feat for a woman in 1908. Unfortunately, both she and her husband had a need to sneer at Kitty with her fancy fee-paying education at George Watson's Ladies College. After all it had only led to her becoming a typist or secretary at best. They in contrast had both been members of the well-respected teaching profession.

Perhaps Kitty had not been without fault either, and no doubt had provoked her in-laws by behaving in the manner of a lady who had just found herself living 'in the sticks'. She was also stupidly inclined to put her nose in the air and dismiss the citizens of Aberdeen as 'plebeian philistines', which did not exactly improve the situation. Ironically, her mother-in-law was in fact one of the most cultured people she was to come across and later proved to be the greatest influence on her granddaughter's life, when it came to her love of literature.

As to divulging the truth about her own parents, Kitty was never to do so. Instead, she said they had both died of black water fever when she was young. Where she got the idea for this fabrication she could not remember. Perhaps she had read it in some novel or seen it in a film, but anyhow it sounded vaguely exotic.

On finding herself in this new and not altogether happy world, Kitty longed to be back with her friends and with her aunts again. These people she was now living amongst were alien to her and not very welcoming. She did, however, appreciate the kindness shown to both of her children by her mother-in-law, who was particularly fond of Norman, despite their not being related. When he sang the words of 'You are My Sunshine' to her, her heart melted. Her husband, however, was cold to the little boy.

During their stay at the Braes, one of the happier moments was the day on which Fergie came home with a white rough-haired dog of many breeds, who was to become an important part of the family for many years. He named him Rex.

Eventually the little bungalow at Bucksburn was ready for the family to move into and, although a modest abode of two bedrooms, a living room, bathroom and kitchen, it was theirs to enjoy as they pleased. Soon Kitty was distempering the walls, (blue with silver splodges in the children's bedroom, pink with gold in theirs) and Fergie was cultivating the garden, growing gooseberries, strawberries, raspberries, blackcurrants and rhubarb, as well as potatoes, carrots, turnips and runner beans.

They also got to know their next-door neighbours, the Blackadders and the Rosses, two young couples of similar ages to Fergie and Kitty, with whom they soon made firm friends. Many happy evenings were spent in each other's houses and, during the day, the wives would drink coffee together in between doing their housework and shopping. Every day, Kitty would walk Rex down to the local grocer's shop to buy the daily goods necessary to feed the family. She enjoyed preparing meals such as shepherd's pie, fish pie, macaroni cheese, rhubarb and custard and, as a treat on Sundays, a roast and a trifle although, as the story went, one day, being hungry and finding the meal not ready, the children ate some of Rex's biscuits and enjoyed them, particularly the black ones.

Friends, such as those from the bank or with whom Fergie played hockey, cricket and tennis, came to visit. Kitty got to know the mothers of her children's school pals and sometimes they too would visit. Fergie's parents would come over on Sundays and, when Mr Mackie died in 1948, his wife would often bring along another relation. Also, Auntie Chrissie would come up from Edinburgh quite regularly, for she was now living alone in St Albans Road, Minnie having also died that year.

By then, Norman was already attending the Aberdeen Grammar School in town. For a short time it was fee-paying, which meant he was accepted despite living in the shire. Soon, however, it became non-fee paying and then only accepting boys from the city but by then he was already a pupil. The High School for Girls operated on similar lines, which meant that by the time his sister was to go to school she was not accepted and instead attended the private Albyn School for Girls. To Kitty, having been brought up in Edinburgh where a great deal of snobbery had been attached to schools, she believed going to private schools was imperative. However, she quickly learned there was not such a distinction in Aberdeen.

Every morning, eight-year-old Norman went by tram to school, sometimes accompanied by Fergie but more often by himself, and a year later his sister would be taken by Kitty to Union Street to catch a tram to go to school unaccompanied. Norman would be dressed in a navy blazer, shorts and cap, while his sister's bottle green uniform included a little kilt attached to a bodice was worn in winter. In summer, the uniform was a green and white checked frock and Panama hat. Kitty always made sure her children's feet were carefully measured before buying Clark's Start-Rite sandals, for she had a fear they would develop hammer toes as she had done through lack of care in her own childhood.

Sometimes, Fergie would take the children with him to fish in the nearby river, to sit on the bank with their little rods while patiently – or in some cases not so patiently – waiting for a fish to nibble. Other times they would 'guddle' for tadpoles and take them home to watch them turn into frogs. In the summer, the family would often go down to Aberdeen Beach and spend hours visiting the carnival, riding on painted horses on the carousel, driving 'dodgem 'cars, and rolling pennies to win a cuddly toy or tadpole. Then they would laugh as they tried to eat pink candy floss which stuck to their cheeks, or ice-cream which dribbled down their chins. If the days were warm, they would mingle with the crowds on the beach, and paddle in the freezing North Sea. Actual holidays were spent either at Cruden Bay or North Berwick, but Stonehaven was a favourite place, for there they could swim in the warmer water of the swimming pool in their prickly, uncomfortable swimming costumes, while listening to strains of 'She Wears Red Feathers and a Huly Huly Skirt' and other such popular songs blaring out from the loudspeakers.

Kitty's special holiday was the yearly Easter visit to Edinburgh, when for a week she would take the children with her to stay at her aunt's house in St Albans Road, there to be thoroughly spoiled. Each morning, the kind old lady would bring each of them tea in bed, and after breakfast the children would join their friends, Michael and Alice who lived in the road, to climb Blackford Hill, feed the ducks by the Pond or simply play 'Hide and Seek' or 'What's the Time, Mr Wolf?' in the road. Of course, being Easter, one of the highlights of the holiday was to go up Blackford Avenue to the 'shop up the steps' and choose either a chocolate Easter egg or bunny.

Meanwhile, Kitty would go into town to meet her old friends for coffee at McVities or Fullers and afterwards visit Darlings, Jenners, Forsyths or Binns. Every spring Auntie Chrissie would give her a generous allowance to kit herself out in the latest fashions and to visit a hair salon to style her hair. Her aunt well understood there was little money coming into the house in Sclattie Park, for a bank teller's salary was small and, knowing well how much her niece had always appreciated the little extravagances of life, she was delighted to provide some of them. In 1949 for example Kitty had longed to wear Dior's New Look but, because clothes were still rationed at that time, most women could only dream of such fashion. With extra coupons supplied by her aunt, she managed to buy a couple of New Look clothes. On returning home to Aberdeen, Kitty would unwisely display her latest purchases and then, unsurprisingly, be left to endure her mother-in-law's snide comments. One particular comment frequently made was that Kitty should learn "to cut your coat according to your cloth".

During these Easter breaks in Edinburgh, Chrissie would babysit in the evenings to allow Kitty to be free to dine with friends in town at the fashionable Epicure, At other times, all of them would go to the Dominion Cinema in Church Hill to see a film such as 'Singing in the Rain' after which there was dancing around each lamppost and tree on the way home.

In their little home in Bucksburn, the family spent many happy hours together, even during the bad winter of 1947, when coal was short and over two million workers were laid off. On looking back on those years between 1947 and 1951, Kitty was later to realise that they had been the best she and Fergie were to spend together.

Then in 1951 all that was to change. An ideal family house in town came on the market. It was in Belvidere Street in the Rosemount area near to schools, the bank and the shops. However, there was just one snag. Fergie could not afford to buy it, despite the Bank's very generous mortgage arrangement offered to its staff. The solution, of course, was simple. His mother would pay off the mortgage and for doing so, come to live with them. Until then she had been living with her sister and husband, but life in their house had been somewhat strained on many occasions. This arrangement would solve everyone's needs.

And so it was that in 1951 the family moved from the little bungalow in Slattie Park to their new terraced home in Belvidere Street, with the Victoria and Westburn Parks at the foot of the street, a variety of shops at the top in Rosemount Place from where the children could either walk to school or take a tram. The house had a living room, lounge, kitchen, bathroom and three bedrooms, leaving two good-sized rooms upstairs for Fergie's mother. With her there, there was a live-in babysitter plus someone who could help the children with their homework. All seemed perfect. Alas, it was not to be.

In the same year, much to the family's delight, the Tories got back into power led once more by Winston Churchill. Britain was a nation of restraint and decency, a country of homemade clothes and home-grown food, of clipped hedges, pressed trousers and high church attendance, of children's comics such as the 'Eagle' and the 'Girl', promising a brighter future. It was after all the second richest county in the world. But many people were bored and resentful, as was the case of Kitty.

Once the children had left the house in the morning, she and her mother-in-law were left together and, coming from such different cultures and having such different values, it was an unhappy arrangement. Both were sharp and sneering, both judgemental and critical of one another and, by the time Fergie and the children came home for lunch, there was usually a tense atmosphere. Fergie was always expected to visit his mother upstairs as soon as he arrived home, which he always did being so subservient to his mother who would often boast how he had never said 'No' to her. Deeply irritated by this, Kitty resented her mother-in-law's presence and power even more.

As time went on, Fergie and Kitty began to grow further and further apart, for all the love and companionship they had once shared it had disappeared. For all that Fergie was still loving, kind and gentle, he had little ambition and, from once being the dashing young major Kitty had met during the War, he was now a poorly-paid bank teller, content simply to fish and play bridge. Kitty on the other hand, being only too well aware that if David had lived she would have been the wife of an engineer in the oil business and perhaps living abroad amongst interesting people, was dissatisfied. Once, she did try to persuade Fergie to apply for a job in Rhodesia, but he would not consider it, feeling obliged to be in Aberdeen for his mother's sake.

Kitty had always thrived on fun and excitement but there was none. All she could do was escape on Saturday afternoons with a friend and their daughters into the imaginary world of glamour and fantasy through going to see 'a picture'. Together they saw every musical film, knew all the words of the songs from 'Carousel', 'A Star is Born' and 'Calamity Jane'. They imagined dancing like Gene Kelly and Fred Astaire, while singing like Doris Day and Judy Garland. Sometimes, they would go to His Majesty's Theatre and attend plays brought up from London such as 'Gigi' with Leslie Caron, 'The South Sea Bubble' with Vivian

Leigh or 'The Devil's Disciple' with Tyrone Power. Afterwards, they would prolong the magic by going round to the stage door to catch a glimpse of the stars coming out.

As in just about every other home at that time, the record player took pride of place beside a pile of 78 rpm records. Fergie would listen to Scottish songs such as 'The Northern Lights of Aberdeen' by Robert Wilson or 'My Love is Like a Red, Red Rose' by Kenneth McKellar, while Kitty and Sylvia enjoyed listening to 'Softly, Softly' by Ruby Murray or anything by Frank Sinatra. Norman too collected records and his choice later included hits such as Bill Hailey's 'Rock Around the Clock' or Elvis Presley's 'Jailhouse Rock'.

During that period, the world awoke to a very special day. Not only had Mount Everest been conquered, but it was also Coronation Day and the young Princess Elizabeth was to become queen. Already, the country had been involved in all kinds of activities to celebrate. Union Jacks waved in the wind and strips of red, white and blue bunting were seen hanging from outside houses in every street in the land, while each child was presented with a tin decorated with pictures of the Queen and the Union Jack in which were found several slim little bars of chocolate.

Their neighbours in Belvidere Street, the Irvines, owned a very small black and white television and so all the family, along with other neighbours, were invited to come and view the crowning of the new Queen; although several weeks later, all pupils in the Aberdeen schools were taken to the Odeon Picture House at Holburn Junction to see the film of the ceremony in full colour.

Each year, Fergie and Kitty would attend bank staff dances with friends, for which she would always buy a new dress. Perhaps these were the most exciting times for her. She could dress up, look glamorous and dance the night away. One year, however, looking particularly attractive in a long white satin gown worn with green gloves, she was overjoyed to meet an old friend from her Edinburgh past, who now held a senior position at the head office of the bank there. Perhaps she flirted rather too much with him and perhaps enjoyed causing mischief by flaunting her connections with the man, but a female friend became so jealous that, on retiring to the ladies' cloakroom, the so-called friend took out her bright red lipstick and scored it right down the back of Kitty's dress.

Kitty found life boring during those gloomy days of the fifties. She felt like a caged animal and, while never wishing to leave the children, she longed for another life full of excitement and glamour. Shelagh Delaney, the writer of the play, "A Taste of Honey" had been quoted as saying, "People of my age know what they want to do like a horse on a tether sort of jerking about and waiting for someone to cut the tether and let them off." It was a perfect description of Kitty's predicament.

Then twelve years later in July 1957, while half listening to her mother-in-law again delivering the same advice about "cutting your coat according to your cloth", the telephone rang. It was a call from Edinburgh. Auntie Chrissie had fallen and hit her head on the fireplace. She had been found by her cleaning lady who had very soon summoned help but, in spite of quickly being taken to hospital in Drummond Place, Kitty's favourite aunt had died.

She was stunned by the news for she loved and owed so much to Auntie Chrissie. This kind lady had rescued her from an uncertain and frightening childhood, taken her on holidays abroad, walks in the hills, trips to the seaside, visits to theatres and concert halls, but above all, had shown her love and had provided her with the security she had so desperately needed. She had meant so much to Kitty and would be sorely missed by all the family for her gentle mischievous smile and constant but pleasant smell of pan drops and barley sugar, which she had sucked over the years to relieve the pain of an ulcer. Now, Auntie Chrissie was no more.

After the funeral, Kitty got on with the practical job of clearing the house in St Albans Road, her home for so long, in order for it to be sold. And so in June of that year, she went down to Edinburgh alone because the first thing she wished to do was to bin all items pertaining to her mother and father, in fear of anyone in the family discovering the truth. She carefully examined the house for any scrap of evidence relating to her parents, be it books, letters or photographs, and all were discarded or burned before the children came down to join her. She even made sure the family bibles, always once so carefully preserved in the cupboard in the front room, were destroyed and, now that Auntie Chrissie was dead, she made sure that no one would ever know the truth.

When the rest of the family did go down to join her in the July of that year, they helped her sort out the furniture, paintings, crockery and silver. Kitty had no use for the two horsehair-stuffed Queen Anne chairs, which had belonged to the family for generations and that had sat in the drawing room, the larger one with arms suitable for the gentleman and the smaller one without arms for the lady, presumably to accommodate her wide skirts. These were sent to the salesroom along with heavy beds, wardrobes, chests of drawers and dressing tables, and, with their sale, Kitty later bought a comfortable modern three-piece suite.

Kitty did, however, keep some of the beds and wardrobes together with a Sheraton games table, eight Regency dining chairs, and a grandfather clock which she thought had belonged to her grandmother, Chrissie Waugh, or great grandmother, Elizabeth Dodds. She also decided to keep the monogrammed silver which had also belonged to various members of the family, as well as the snuff box perhaps belonging to James Turnbull, her great-great-great-grandfather, and the calling card box belonging to the Rev. Andrew Dodds, her great-grandfather. As for the cutlery, candlesticks and wine holders, also monogrammed with Ds, As and Ts, she had no idea to whom they had belonged but she did know that the Dickson tea service was valuable, having been told so by her aunts on a number of occasions and so she kept that. The aunts had often talked to her about their ancestors, but she, like most young people, had barely listened at the time.

The rest of the furniture and furnishings were dispatched to Lyle and Turnbull's auction rooms, along with a certain hideous painting which had a slash in it that had hung for years above the mantelpiece in the morning room. None of her aunts had ever explained to her how the gash in the canvas had got there. She did, however, keep a picture of her grandmother, whom she vaguely remembered, sitting with a child in her lap.

Along with a few miniatures of various people, including one of Mungo Park, she also kept a simple Sheraton work basket with its pink plaited-silk basket. On opening it, Sylvia found various letters and on examination found them to be written by various members of the family throughout the years. There was also a whole clutch of letters tied together with a pink ribbon, which had been written by someone during the Napoleonic Wars. Kitty had some vague recollection of having been told they were from some relation who had been a surgeon at that time, and was ready to bin the lot until Sylvia stopped her from doing so.

Also in the basket was an old 'Scotsman' newspaper cutting dated 10th March 1955, which did interest her. It described how a Mrs Dora Noyce had been jailed for six months for keeping and managing a brothel in her respectable house in 17 Danube Street, Stockbridge. What was so strange and so amusing was that also in the workbasket was another letter written in the 1880s from her grandmother's aunt, Christina Bilton, to her niece, headed with the same address. What would that upright Victorian lady have thought if she had known her home would eventually become a brothel? Auntie Chrissie must have kept the article and had a quiet chuckle to herself.

In time, Kitty received the contents of her aunt's will from the family lawyers in Perth, J & J Miller from which she learned of the complicated Turner Trust and that she was to be its sole beneficiary. She realised that, together with the proceeds from the sale of the house, she was now to be "comfortably well off" and so she vowed there and then to take her mother-in-law's advice. She would certainly enjoy "cutting her coat according to her cloth", especially now that the cloth had immensely increased in value.

Chapter 3

1967: A Time of Change

"As the present now
Will later be past
The order is
Rapidly fadin'
And the first one now
Will later be last
For the times they are a-changin'
(Bob Dylan 1964)

Kitty stood in front of the main door of Kings College Chapel and felt good. It was a warm June day in 1965 and Norman, having graduated from Aberdeen University, had just been married. There he stood beside his bride, surrounded by family and friends, while the many photographs were being taken. In her petrol blue silk coat and matching petalled hat, she dutifully lined up with the rest of the family to be photographed beside the newly-weds.

In doing so, she glanced towards the assembled crowd of friends and relatives who had attended the ceremony and who were there to enjoy the happy day, when suddenly she caught sight of an old woman who looked vaguely familiar but was certainly not one of the invited guests. Getting more and more short-sighted as the years went by, she peered again at the figure and, while still smiling for the photographs, realised with horror that she was looking at her mother. Although she had not seen her for many years, she knew it was her. Once again, here she was turning up at a wedding to which she had not been invited, just as she had done in 1939 at Kitty's own first wedding, according to Auntie Chrissie. She may also have been at her second in Blackford in 1942 for all she knew, but here she was again, this time to witness the wedding of her grandson.

In the midst of family, friends and neighbours gathered that day to toast the future success of the young couple, this spectre from the past emerged to cast a shadow on what should have been a perfect day for Kitty. A deep feeling of resentment and anger welled up inside her. How dare this harridan who had blighted her young life presume to show her face at this happy event.

Kitty quickly caught Fergie's eye and pointedly looked towards the uninvited guest. He did not immediately understand what she was trying to convey. However, after the many photographs, chats with well-wishers, and waves to the happy couple as they got into their taxi to take them to the reception, Kitty turned to him with a quiet but desperate plea, "Do something, for God's sake. Get rid of her. I don't want her near me. Tell her she's not welcome. Please, Fergie. She mustn't get into the reception at the hotel. Why does she have to be here? Does she do it to annoy me? I can't stand the woman!"

Fergie, of course, immediately knew what she was talking about, for he was one of the very few who had been told the truth about Kitty's parents. He could hardly forget the article published several years before in the 'Perth Advertiser' and then 'The Aberdeen Press and Journal' which had read:

"Perth Woman's Husband Presumed to Have Died

A presumption of death order, which was sought by a 72-year old Perth woman whose husband disappeared 40 years ago after telling her that he might join the Foreign Legion, was granted by Sheriff A.M. Prain at Perth yesterday. The action was brought by Mrs Georgina Anderson Flannery , c/o 8 St Ann's South Street, Perth. She petitioned the court to find that John Flannery, last heard of at Drumbrae Road, Barnton, Edinburgh, had disappeared; that the date on which he was last known to be alive was in September 1923; and that he died or must be presumed dead in September 1930. In her condescendence, the pursuer said that she was married in Edinburgh on 27 November 1916. Flannery was then a lieutenant in the Lovat Scouts and, after their marriage; she lived with her mother at 22 Hillview, Blackhall, Edinburgh. Her husband stayed with her when his military duties permitted. In 1918, he went to with the Camel Corps, and thereafter served with the Indian Army. In 1923 he was cashiered from the Indian Army for drunkenness, she alleged. By that time, he had attained the rank of captain. He came home and lived with the pursuer in Edinburgh for a few months, then disappeared. He was aged 33 at the time. Before he went off, his father, now deceased, had suggested that he go abroad and Flannery had said he might join the Foreign Legion. She had made an effort to trace him, but no news had been heard of him since."

Kitty had been horrified at the article in general and at the inaccuracies in particular but hoped no one would connect her with it. She was glad that Auntie Chrissie was dead by the time the article had appeared, for it would have greatly distressed her. At the time she had no intention of contacting her mother, feeling she owed her nothing. She was just an embarrassment.

Fergie did somehow manage to make contact with this mother-in-law he had never met until that day and send her on her way. Always known for his gentleness and tact, he managed to persuade her to leave them alone.

Ina was never again to be seen by any of the family for in the following year, Kitty was contacted by the Perth family solicitors informing her that her mother had passed away in a mental asylum at Murthly in Perthshire. Reluctantly she attended the cremation with Fergie, signed the death certificate, while noticing that it declared her mother was still married, and vowed never to forgive her. Nor would she ever tell her children the truth about their grandmother.

But those were The Sixties and the times were changing as Bob Dylan's song of 1964 had predicted. The traditions of hierarchies of social class inherited from medieval landowners, industrial capitalism and imperial administration began to wobble and social, political and cultural change became evermore apparent. Those were the years during which abortion and homosexuality became legal, capital punishment was abolished and theatre censorship came to an end. No longer were debutantes, upper-class young ladies, presented at Court to the Queen; and no longer did young men do National Service. The Pill was introduced, which changed people's behaviour and attitudes to sex forever; meantime, church attendances went down. The automatic deference to authority – the police, judges, teachers and parents, members of the church and of parliament – began to erode.

Also, the term 'teenager' had begun to emerge but, as before, the music and dress came from America, influenced by rock and roll pop stars such as Bill Haley and Elvis Presley. Women abandoned gloves, hats and corsets, and instead wore dirndl skirts with many petticoats in the style of Sandra Dee. Young men sported the same style of jackets and flannels as their fathers before them, but carefully combed their hair into kiss curls like Bill Haley or D.A.s (ducks' arses) like Elvis, not a style favoured by their fathers.

But Britain soon found its own icons in the form of Lonnie Donegan, Cliff Richard and eventually in the worldwide sensations of the Beatles and the Rolling Stones. The country discovered its own music and its own dress. The Swinging Sixties had arrived and, while only a few young people actually frequented Swinging London and its Carnaby Street, most copied its fashion trends. Mary Quant's many coloured mini-skirts and hot pants appeared on the High Street, as did the hairstyles of Vidal Sassoon.

Every young girl wanted to look like Twiggy while the lads, with their longer hair, kipper ties, psychedelic shirts and flared trousers, aped John Lennon.

The old traditions and beliefs began to retreat while a tide of change swept through society. A new freedom and self-confidence appeared and, just as in Dorothy's world in 'The Wizard of Oz', which changed from monochrome to Technicolor, the bleakness of post-war Britain was transformed into a world of colour and, for the young especially, a land of hope where anything was possible.

In Aberdeen, while certainly many of the old traditions still existed, life began to change there too. Crowds, largely of men, still attended football matches every week at Pittodrie Stadium in support of the Dons, while their wives and daughters still continued to spend their Saturday afternoons flocking to the Odeon or Astoria, the Regal or the Gaumont cinemas to watch their favourite stars in films from Hollywood. Theatre audiences still continued to attend performances of such stars as Alec Finlay, Ricky Fulton or Kenneth McKellar at His Majesty's Theatre or Robert Wilson at the Tivoli Theatre. At the same time, however, performers such as Tommy Steele, Petula Clark, and Gerry and the Pacemakers appeared at the Capitol Cinema, while even the Beatles played at the Beach Ballroom!

On Saturday evenings, students and anyone interested in changing society rushed home to watch 'That Was the Week That Was' on television with David Frost and company entertaining audiences throughout the land with their biting satire on the established power structures. The automatic deference to authority was certainly disappearing. Satire had also begun to emerge in other forms of media such as in 'Private Eye'.

Kitty's life was changing too. She bought herself smart clothes and weekly attended Richie's, the hairdresser. She could now afford to go on holidays with the family to places further afield than Stonehaven and Cruden Bay, and would also holiday regularly with her friend, Rita Davie, to France and to Spain, which suited Fergie as he preferred to go on fishing holidays. Kitty also learned to play bridge with her friends, sometimes in their homes and sometimes at the Aberdeen Bridge Club, although Fergie was the true bridge player and won many competitions over the years. As in the past, Kitty still attended theatres and cinemas, as well as taking part in weekly afternoon conversational French classes and Saturday coffee mornings in the 'Caley' Hotel.

During his time as a pupil at the Grammar School, her son made friends. One was called Peter Walker who lived at the top of Belvidere Street at 250 Rosemount Place. Peter's father, Dickie, was the family's GP and his mother, Rosemary, a pretty lady of similar age to Kitty. Soon the two couples became firm friends and, on some Saturday nights, they would party at the Walkers' home, dancing the night away to the music of Ray Charles, Kenny Ball and Duke Ellington, while drinking copious glasses of whisky and smoking many cigarettes. For both of them, this was a bit of excitement and fun but Fergie's mother, needless to say, thoroughly disapproved of such behaviour.

Rosemary Walker had always provided afternoon tea every day for her husband and four other doctors when they met at the house between morning and evening surgeries. However, eventually she had to stop this because of crippling arthritis and Kitty stepped in to help. It became a task she much enjoyed, for it took her away from the presence of her disapproving mother-in-law, and she spent more and more time with Dickie and the other doctors.

Sadly, in 1963, Rosemary died and only four years later, Fergie also became unwell and was diagnosed with cancer. Always a mild and caring man, gentle and sincere, he was much respected by all those who knew him and would always be remembered as a fine bridge player. He was never happier than when sitting at a card table, a cigarette in one hand and a good set of cards in the other.

What was going on in Kitty's mind and in her heart was difficult to tell. She saw to her husband's practical needs but spent little time by his side. To those around, she appeared unfeeling and perhaps she was. Perhaps life had made her so, having experienced so many tragedies in her young life. It was sad, however, to see no signs of grief for the dying of her partner who had only ever been kind and supportive to her.

In the July of that year, Fergie was taken to Woodend Hospital and died very soon after, aged only 54. His mother, having lost her only son, was heartbroken but her firm faith in God and the afterlife kept her going, and it was she who paid for her son's tombstone to be erected in Springbank Cemetery alongside his father's.

After the funeral, grandmother, mother and daughter spent a miserable week together at Lochearnhead in Perthshire, after which Kitty decided to sell the family home. She would at last be free to live away from her mother-in-law, for whom, although the old lady was 78, she felt no responsibility. She could now find a home for herself somewhere else, which she did with the help of a niece and her bank manager husband who helped her buy a flat in Forest Avenue. There, the old lady managed to look after herself with the help of the couple and her granddaughter Sylvia to do her shopping, and there were always visitors who genuinely enjoyed spending time in her company.

The house in Belvidere Street was soon sold and Kitty bought a flat in St Swithins Street for herself and her daughter. At the same time, she found herself a job working as a shop assistant in Nova in Chapel Street for she had little money left, having spent most of her inheritance and the widow's pension was small. Over only a few years, vast changes had taken place in her life and she was still only 49.

Chapter 4

1980: A Time of Discovery

"Fit's it like being third mate tae an Aiberdeen drifter?"

The remark had been made by one of Dickie's patients one warm sunny afternoon in June 1969, when he and Kitty were sitting with friends and family in the Treetops Hotel. They had just been married in Queens Cross Church. Everyone had laughed that day for this kind of humour was typical of Dickie's own. He didn't mind being referred to as a third mate, nor did she apparently mind being called an "Aberdeen drifter".

Dressed in a fetching coffee-coloured suit and large-brimmed hat, Kitty could not have been happier. All tragedies and deaths appeared to be behind her and she and Dickie were now ready to share their joy openly together. He had always made her laugh and she appreciated his sense of humour, energy and positive attitude to life. In turn, he adored her good looks, snobbery and short-sightedness and was delighted to indulge her every whim, be it in choice of holidays, clothes or redesigning his house. The work on '250', his home and surgery, had begun long before the wedding day and was now almost complete.

Dickie had spent little money over the years in maintaining the house or on the surgery below, so Kitty, now more often known as Kit, was given the freedom to plan and budget as she wished in the redesigning and decorating of her new home. Originally, Dickie and his partner, Hugh, had held their surgeries on the first floor of the building beside the waiting room. How any of the rooms had passed any health and safety inspection was hard to tell for they were so unkempt, no cleaning lady having ever been hired to clean the place. Now the plan was that the three rooms which had housed the two surgeries and the waiting room would become part of the home, while the old kitchen and snug in the basement would become surgeries and waiting room. A full-time receptionist was appointed, together with a daily cleaner to keep the surgeries clean and hygienic. However, despite notices warning of the dangers of smoking, both doctors and receptionist continued to be heavy smokers which left a strong waft of cigarettes to greet the patients as they entered.

Kit took great delight in turning the original waiting room on the first floor into a large kitchen with fitted units, the latest cooker, dishwasher and washing machine, plus a huge fridge. Meanwhile, Hugh's old surgery, the largest room in the house, was converted into a lounge, for which new furniture was bought to be placed alongside her grandfather clock, piano, workbasket and card table. Wall cabinets on either side of the fireplace were erected to display the family silver, while the picture of her grandmother hung on the wall. Dickie's old surgery then became the dining room where her regency chairs, now reupholstered in red and cream stripes, sat round a new rosewood table. On the second and third floors, the bedrooms were also redecorated, and the bathroom updated with a fashionable avocado suite, 'all the rage' at that time. Central heating was also installed but, as Kitty had never been used to such a luxury before, on the first day she made the mistake of turning the temperature up to maximum, thus causing some of her antique furniture to crack.

After all the years of bitterness and sarcasm, the gulf between Kit and her ex-mother-in law began to fade, perhaps because they no longer lived in the same house, or because they didn't have to compete for Fergie's attention. Whatever the reason, the rift began to heal, helped in no small way by Dickie's charm and his liking for the old lady. She in turn appreciated his kindness and knew that this man, while having replaced her son in her daughter-in-law's affections, had always held a great regard for Ferguson. He cheered her up with his humour on his regular visits to her new home, both as her GP and as a friend. Although not amusing at the time, he once made the mistake of prescribing pills for her rheumatism which resulted in the similar effects of taking LSD, causing her to imagine flowers coming out of chimney pots and people's heads. However, as soon as she stopped taking the medicine, she became her old self again, but it prompted Dickie to call her his '80-year-old flower power hippie' from then on. He even invited her to their wedding, but she declined. not because she disapproved but more because of her age.

Kit and Dickie's honeymoon was spent in Aghios Nikolaus in Crete, the choice being prompted by the BBC programme 'The Lotus Eaters' which had been filmed on that island. On the way back, the newly-weds spent a couple of nights at a Mayfair hotel while visiting Harrods and dining one evening on the Thames before returning home to Aberdeen to a busy life. Surgeries would begin at 8:30a.m. until coffee time, after which Dickie and Hugh would visit the elderly or housebound patients until lunchtime. The break for them came when they were joined by other GPs for afternoon tea, during which time they were still 'on call', before beginning the evening surgery at 5p.m. In those days patients just turned up at the surgeries without an appointment, meaning surgeries continued until the last person left.

On Wednesday evenings, Dickie and Kit would always go to the Treetops Hotel where Stuart Spence, a patient and the hotel's manager, would serve them their favourite Chicken Maryland dish, whatever time they arrived. On some other evenings, they would join friends at the nearby Atholl Hotel and, like everyone else in those days, think nothing of driving home after more than several glasses of whisky.

Kit was never happier in her life, nor indeed more attractive. As someone described her, she was like "the cat that had got the cream". No longer did she have to live with a difficult mother-in-law and her financial worries were over. Finally, she could relax and enjoy life, not quite becoming a Greta Garbo, but as near as made her very happy.

She continued meeting friends, playing bridge and taking her dog for walks. She had just bought a little West Highland puppy and had called it Jenny. This fluffy little ball of mischief was much-loved and even forgiven when she chewed an expensive pair of red Rayne shoes Kit had bought in Harrods, while on honeymoon.

On quiet evenings, the couple would lounge in front of the television after the surgery, each holding a whisky in one hand and a cigarette in the other. While not a ballet fan, Dickie did watch Margot Fonteyn and her young partner, the Russian dancer, Rudolf Nureyev, perform 'The Sleeping Beauty', while declaring that the dancers, based on what he saw, must be having an affair.

Although extremely happy, not everything went perfectly for Kit. One evening, while dining on a cheese fondue washed down with cider, she developed tremendous stomach cramps and was swiftly taken to hospital only to discover she had Crohn's Disease. Although very serious at the time, after an operation and appropriate medication to control it, she successfully managed the ailment during the many years to come.

Another infliction was her short-sightedness, and Dickie took great delight in mimicking her making bridge appointments. He would stand with bottom out and nose nearly touching the diary as she tried to write dates.

Then on 20th July 1969, the couple shared great news with the rest of the world. It was the day that Apollo 11 landed the lunar module 'Eagle' on the moon. Both were engrossed in the television programme, broadcast to a worldwide audience, of the moon landing made by mission commander, Neil Armstrong, and pilot, Buzz Aldrin. Like everyone else, they were thrilled at being able to see Armstrong step onto the lunar surface, while describing the event as "one small step for man, one giant leap for mankind", and to watch the television footage of the two men spending two hours on the moon collecting soil samples and planting a specially-designed flag on the lunar surface. They heard Armstrong describe the experience as "magnificent desolation" when the two astronauts returned to Earth four days later, when they were to receive a heroes' welcome from President Nixon and the world.

On the 28th April of the following year, another exciting thing happened, this time closer to home. The local newspaper, 'The Aberdeen Press and Journal', announced that oil had been detected in the North Sea. This discovery was to put Aberdeen on the map, for in the coming years it was to become known as the oil capital of Europe. A consortium headed by Phillips Petroleum had discovered an oil field with 2.8 billion barrels of reserve, lying hard upon the dividing line between Britain and Norway. Soon after, BP discovered a bigger field on Britain's side which would become known as the Forties Field, to be followed by an even bigger discovery made by Shell International to become known as the Brent Field.

Up until then, the economy of the Silver City had for so long depended on fishing, farming and the granite industry, but the famous Rubislaw Quarry was closed on the very day oil had been discovered. Until that point, Aberdeen had slipped economically into fourth place in Scotland behind Edinburgh, Glasgow and Dundee, but this was soon to be reversed as tangible signs of oil began to mushroom. Now not only did theatres, football stadia, dance halls and cinemas provide entertainment as before, but roulette tables began to appear as the new night clubs emerged such as the Blue Chip, the Cheval and the Maverick. Union Street changed overnight and shops began selling mink coats and expensive diamond rings, while rednecks walking down the street in buckskin jackets, Stetson hats and cowboy boots became a familiar sight. Thousands of Americans and other nationalities came crowding into the Granite City, the offshore workforce rising at one stage to over 30,000. Hotels and restaurants did a roaring trade, especially as many of the divers and drillers came alone and ate out when not working offshore. Not only did shops, hotels and restaurants open, new schools were planned for the many children who had come to the city with their parents.

But, as well as bringing great wealth to the city, the discovery of oil also brought problems. Those not in the oil industry had to face the increased cost of housing, and so many Aberdonians found themselves priced out of the property market and forced to move out of the city. Meanwhile, what had once been large private residences in Queens Road and elsewhere now became offices for Conoco, Marathon and Brit Oil, while new offices for Shell and BP were built nearer to the harbour.

British European Airways moved the headquarters of its entire helicopter service from Gatwick to Aberdeen Airport, because of the volume of work involved in carrying personnel to and from the oil rigs. Bases and new trends of ships began to emerge. Even prostitutes claimed they were doing better business in Aberdeen than in London.

In the midst of all this, Dickie and his partner, Hugh, found themselves busy providing health insurance certificates for the oil company workers, as well as generally tending to the health of all the new arrivals.

But it would take another five years before the oil began to flow. The thick black liquid, which lay within layers of rock, had to be extracted and so gigantic platforms with as much steel as that in the Forth Railway Bridge were built and then towed out to the angry waters of the North Sea. Beyond all that, drilling operations had to be investigated to reach down and shatter the rock far below.

During all this immediate excitement in Aberdeen, Kit and Dickie watched a televised funeral taking place much further away – that of Dickie's hero, the jazz trumpeter, Louis Armstrong. Dickie himself had been no mean jazz pianist and had always loved the music of Duke Ellington and Louis Armstrong. While the trumpeter and his fellow musicians had themselves played at many funerals, when it came to Louis Armstrong's own, it was a time of silent mourning, other than Peggy Lee's rendition of 'The Lord's Prayer'. However, later, many television programmes dedicated to the trumpeter were seen, and songs such as 'When the Saints Go Marching In', 'Hello Dolly', and, of course, 'It's a Wonderful World' were heard. This death took place in July 1971.

No one was to know that six months later Dickie's own death from lung cancer was to follow, only less than three years after marrying Kit. Hardy to the end, he carried on working until six days before his death and, while yellow with jaundice and heavily drugged, he listened patiently to the ailments of his patients, one even complaining of an ingrown toenail. But he knew the end had come when, on New Year's Day, he handed someone his glass of whisky for he no longer was able to drink his favourite tipple. Three days later, Kit awoke to find him lying dead beside her with Jenny, their little dog, jumping up on the bed and licking his face.

Arrangements were soon underway and a heavily-attended funeral took place. Not everyone could fit into the crematorium and many patients had to stand outside to pay their last respects to their hardy little doctor who had made them laugh. Everyone who knew him was devastated to hear of his death.

Sadly, Dickie did not manage to attend the marriage of his only son, Peter, which took place later that year, and his absence was acutely felt by all who did attend that summer wedding. Not only did he miss that occasion, but also later the birth of his only granddaughter, Rosie, called after his first wife.

Something Dickie also missed, which would have intrigued him, was the momentous day for Aberdeen and indeed for the country when, in November 1975, oil began to flow from the depths of the North Sea to the BP refinery at Grangemouth, very soon to produce four thousand barrels of oil per day. He would have been so interested in such an achievement.

Throughout these years, Mrs Mackie continued to live in her flat while still enjoying reasonably good health. She had witnessed a great many changes, from the time of standing with her father on a hillside in 1901 to watch the bonfires burning along the north east coast, signalling the Relief of Mafeking, to the moon landing in 1969. Then in 1976, she succumbed to pneumonia and died aged 86. Death held no fear for her, for her belief in her Lord and the afterlife was unshaken.

Kit, meanwhile, always a survivor, was once again a widow.

Chapter 5

2005: A Time to Say Goodbye

Having sold 250 Rosemount Place, Kit decided to stay in Aberdeen and had moved into a pleasant sunny first-floor flat in the suburb of Cults with its two bedrooms and south facing living room overlooking the hills beyond. From there she was able to walk along the disused railway line with her little dog, Jenny, and visit Sylvia and family. Her grandson, Michael, had been born in 1980 and later Norman and his wife, Elin, had two daughters, Rachael and Anna, who lived in Chester.

Aberdeen was still the booming city of oil with its workers earning 18% more than their counterparts in other parts of the country. The industry was giving work to 52,000 people and, with upwards of 20,000 men working offshore, Aberdeen Airport was on a course to become the biggest helicopter base in the world. At that time, no women were working offshore as it was deemed to be unlucky. By 1990, the harbour was holding a huge fleet of supply vessels, and the city had become a major European port with bases for the oil companies of the world.

While providing well-paid jobs for those in the industry, there were also casualties. Lonely wives were left behind when their husbands went offshore and they found themselves in what one wife described as a place of "miserable weather and grey buildings giving a bleak outlook on life". Such was the loneliness and desperation of many of these wives that many marriages came to an end until, in 1972, a group of women set up the Petroleum Wives Club at Kippie Lodge in Milltimber near to Cults, all having the oil and gas industry in common. It offered friendship to those who had been posted to Aberdeen and the surrounding areas and, by arranging activities and events, it enabled its members to get to know one another as well as to raise money for local charities. The Club was a lifeline for many of these women, for not all Aberdonians had made them feel welcome. Despite the affluence which came to the people of the city, there was in some quarters a feeling of resentment towards these newcomers and their foreign ways.

One amusing story which emerged from those days was of a well-meaning Aberdeen lady who did try to make her new neighbour welcome. He was a deep sea diver who had just arrived from Texas, and she invited him to a dinner party one evening in her Rubislaw Den South house together with other guests. When it was time to sit down and dine, the newly arrived guest took his tobacco pouch out of his mouth and laid it on the side plate, his Stetson hat still on his head much to the surprise of the circumspect Aberdonians.

Although some of these so-called 'incomers' brought their families, many came alone and, although many were brave well-paid men doing dangerous jobs, they were often lonely. A sad familiar sight to see in expensive restaurants was that of those men drinking much, but eating little; often leaving behind a half-eaten plate of excellent food into which a cigarette butt had been stubbed.

Experienced divers came from all over the world in the early days, before the building of the gigantic platforms took place. These brave men worked hard, going down to the deep dangerous surroundings of the North Sea. The oil and gas industry was certainly a well-paid one, but it could also be dangerous. By

1978, 40 men had died in the North Sea and, in 1986, disaster struck the helicopter service when a Chinook, coming to land in Shetland from the Shell Brent field, plunged into the sea, leaving 45 dead. However, the biggest disaster was yet to come.

One balmy evening in July 1988, the Piper Alpha platform exploded. To begin with, the reports described the difficulties the rescue helicopters were having in trying to land on the platform because of the extreme heat and smoke. Eventually, pictures came through of scenes outside the Aberdeen Royal Infirmary where the helicopters were arriving and unloading exhausted survivors, some walking, some on stretchers, their faces blackened with smoke, while yet others, with tin foil wrapped around their burns, were being quickly taken to the intensive care wards. Plastic surgeons were flown in from different parts of the country to help with the many skin grafts that were to take place.

Rescue boats and helicopters did manage to rescue 62 survivors, most of whom had found escape routes across scorching hot decks before jumping from a great height into the dark, cold water below. Those who had stayed in the accommodation module, stood no chance of surviving, their living quarters having plunged to the bottom of the sea.

As Bill Mackie was to write in his book, 'The Oilman', "It marked the end of a romanticised dream of an industry known to the uninitiated only through the celluloid glamour of Hollywood. Suddenly, it had become shockingly and brutally real."

Later, Kit would often go to Hazlehead Park to let Michael have fun jumping on the trampolines, and while there would sometimes visit the Rose Garden. There stood the stark sculpture depicting three oil workers erected on a pink granite plinth, a memorial to the oilmen who lost their lives that night in the biggest tragedy in the history of the oil industry.

Kit enjoyed her life in Cults and continued to shop, socialise and play bridge there, as well as attending functions in support of the Tory Party. Of course, several years before she had made her home there, Britain had voted in its first female prime minister and she shared many of Margaret Thatcher's values. She agreed with the aim of creating a society in which Victorian values were expressed through secure marriages, self-reliance and savings, restraint, good neighbourliness and hard work. Now, being a respectable, comfortably well-off member of Aberdeen society, she thoroughly approved of these sentiments.

One event particularly delighted her. Michael Heseltine, the then Secretary of State for Business, Energy and Industrial Strategy, came to speak at the local Tory party conference at the nearby Marcliffe Hotel and of course she attended. However, on being quizzed about the event after it was over and asked what the politician had said, she could give little information other than a detailed description of the delicious lunch that had been served.

In her 70s, she and Sylvia would go on holiday and visit such capital cities as London, Paris, Rome, and Vienna, and as she became frailer, chose to go to places nearer home such as the Lake District and Pitlochry. While there they would visit theatres, art galleries, castles and cathedrals, always staying at the best of hotels and dining in grand restaurants.

But perhaps the most memorable holiday for Kit was the one in London when she met her hero, Frank Sinatra. Having bought tickets for one of his concerts held at the Albert Hall, Sylvia and she were sipping their gins and tonic before the concert began, when a side door opened and in walked the star surrounded by bodyguards. Several people in wheelchairs were already assembled ready to greet the singer who came and kissed everyone in the chairs. Full of charm and with that famous smile, Sinatra wooed the elderly women roundabout. Kit would always remember that, while his hair had obviously been replanted and his skin looked like leather, the eyes were still as blue and twinkling as ever

During their last holiday together, they visited her beloved Edinburgh once more and even returned to St Albans Road. With the help of her stick, she made her way to the gate. Now there was a high hedge surrounding the front garden and a bright red seat sat in front of what had been her old bedroom window. The front door was closed, barring the view inside the flat but she thought it better not to see inside. Best to remember her home as it was and to remember the happy times she had spent there.50 years had passed since she had said goodbye to the house, when Auntie Chrissie had died. She took one last look at the home which had meant so much to her and then slowly made her way back to the car.

It was on that same last holiday that they also visited the Borders, the home of their ancestors. After a brief visit to Selkirk and an inspection of the statue of Mungo Park standing outside the Anderson family's home – now council offices – they managed to find their way to Hassendeanburn to where the original Hassendeanburn House had once stood. Now some attractive houses had been built in its grounds amongst some rather fine old trees, no doubt planted by the Dickson Nurseries.

She breathed in the peace of the countryside. So this was the place where the Dickson and Turnbull families had lived. On looking towards the river at the bottom of the garden, she remembered a tale told to her by her aunts. Once a church with its graveyard had stood on a projecting point on the north bank, until one night an unusually high flood had torn open the graves and swept the remains of the dead away. Now, however, only a sand bank remained, presumably where the Church had once stood, but overlooked by the same hills and beside the same river that would continue to glide on and on into the future.

Epilogue

On that sunny summer's morning, while standing on the wild and wind-blown summit of Blackford Hill, Norman and Sylvia marvelled at the spectacular views across the city, while also remembering their childhood spent so often climbing the hill.

While Edinburgh appeared tranquil and orderly that morning, its history could not have been described as such. It had been one of crime and culture, poverty and pageantry, torture and tragedy, religion and riots, fires and festivals, deaths and diseases, murders and mayhem. While being home to kings and queens, philosophers and scientists, artists and poets, it had also been so to murderers and swindlers, witches and wizards.

Slowly they removed the lid of the urn and emptied its contents on the ground. Kit had returned to her beloved Edinburgh.

And what of her father, who had left her and her mother in Edinburgh in 1923 never to be seen again? Later it was discovered that Jack had made his way to Liverpool from where he had sailed as an unmarried passenger on the 'Digby' to Halifax, Canada, and then on to New Zealand. There, in Wellington in December 1929, he had married, thus committing bigamy, and the following year became a father once more to a baby daughter, who in turn became a mother of three children.

In 1980, in New Zealand, Jack Flannery died. Meanwhile in Aberdeen, in the very same year, his first great-grandson, Michael, was born.

Author's Note

This book came about after I had found letters dating back to the Napoleonic Wars when helping my mother clear out her dead aunt's house in 1957. They were difficult to read because they were cross written by an army surgeon, Dr Andrew Anderson, while serving in Spain and Portugal during the Peninsular Wars and had been sent to his brother, Dr Thomas Anderson, who lived in Selkirk. They inspired me to begin researching my family history and very soon I discovered that the writer was the twin brother of George, my direct ancestor. I had already known there was some connection between my family and the explorer, Mungo Park, but then I discovered he had married these brothers' sister, Alice Anderson.

From there my research took me to visiting various parts of Scotland and to meeting and writing to many interesting people, some of whom turned out to be distant relations. Tim Anderson was one. He was the direct descendant of the writer of the letters. Barb Cullen from Hailfax, Canada, was another. She and I shared Turnbull ancestry. However, the final piece of the jigsaw – and also the most meaningful piece of information -came from New Zealand from Alex McClymont. It turned out that my grand-father was his too. Alex also provided me with the name of my mother's cousin, Seamus Flannery, who managed to dispel many of the family myths I had been fed as a child. While learning about the Flannery family, on our visit to him and his wife, Maggie, in their charming home in Cornwall, my husband and I also enjoyed stories of Seamus' life as a film designer, his having designed the Wicker Man for the film of that name.

The more I researched, the more I longed to know what these ancestors of mine were like, particularly the seven women of the previous seven generations who had gone before me. Certainly, there were letters written to them and a poem by one of them, but other than that I only knew the facts about them – when and where they were born, lived and died, even for some discovering their wills, but I did not really know them – their thoughts, their feelings, their fears, their ambitions. And so I decided to create their characters and write their story. This book therefore is intended as a novel melding fact with fiction, the broad outline of the story and most of the details being true. Archibald Dickson's catalogues did and still exist; Mungo Park did fall in love with Alice and wrote her touching love letters which also still exist; Charles Darwin did intend to visit Archibald Turnbull in Perth that day but missed him and instead met John Anderson, Archibald's nephew. All these facts are true but the book should be read as historical fiction, intended in part as an act of homage to these seven women who went before me.

Acknowledgments

"A Scots Saga" has taken several years to complete and on my journey I have met many people without whom it would never have been written.

For help with my research, I must thank Alice Gunn, Juline Baird, Susan Donaldson, Hannah Newson, Adam Hillhouse and Elaine Elliot at the Heritage Hub, Hawick; Hilary White, Angus Wark, Alison Metcalf and Hazel Stewart at the National Library of Scotland; Alison Lindsay at General Register House; Betty Hendry of Inverclyde Libraries; Ronald Morrison of the Borders Family History Society; Fiona Hooper of George Watson's College Library; and Estela Dukan, assistant librarian at the Royal College of Physicians Edinburgh

I am also indebted to my newly found family members, namely Tim Anderson, for sharing his publication "Letters of Andrew Anderson Soldier and Surgeon", and Barb Cullen for being such an entertaining companion as we tramped around the various graveyards in search of our Turnbull family. A particular thank you must go to Alex McClymont and to Seamus Flannery for supplying the final missing pieces of the Flannery family jigsaw.

Thanks must also go to Kirsty Macdonald and Kate Porteous for their care and guidance in the writing of the text, as well as to Duncan McKay for his patience and understanding during the publication of the book.

My greatest gratitude, however, must go to my own immediate family. I owe much to Michael, my son, for his advice and patience, particularly on his often being reminded that he should have been born a girl and called Christian for the saga to have continued.

Above all, my final thanks must go to Peter, my late husband, for accompanying me on all these many visits to places and people of much interest to me but little to him and for his being such a long suffering and stimulating companion throughout the whole journey.